the challenge

the challenge

TONY TREVITHICK

 POND VIEW

ISBN 9781871044362

 POND VIEW

is an imprint of
Forward Press Ltd.

Printed in Great Britain

First published in 2004 by

forward**press**

Forward Press Ltd.
Remus House, Peterborough PE2 9JX
www.forwardpress.co.uk

With my sincere thanks to my whole family for their patience and loving support, and to Grace for her hard work and encouragement.

INTRODUCTION

OFTEN, at the beginning of a difficult pastoral conversation, a person will say to me: 'I do not know where to begin'. The set answer, of course, is: 'begin at the beginning'. However, with regard to the life of Jesus, what is the beginning? Is it the moment of birth? Is it the moment of conception? Is it the moment when God decided to reveal Himself in human form?

Most people, when asked to close their eyes and think of God, have an image on the screen of their mind of Jesus. Perhaps it is the memory of a picture of Jesus from a child's Bible or a picture that they saw on a church vestry wall. Those pictures are, of course, artists' impressions, for we have no description of the physical appearance of Jesus in the New Testament. We assume, from the absence of such comments, that He was 'Mr Average', a typical Jew of His day.

It is, therefore, easier to begin the story from the moment of His appearance at the Jordan River, at the beginning of His ministry, when we have detailed descriptions of what happened. What is known before that is shrouded in myth and legend. What we assume is that at some point He grew as a normal baby in Mary's womb and that she gave birth to Him in the town of Bethlehem in Judea. He was a complete and normal human being and grew up in Nazareth where His father had a carpentry business. When Jesus reached the age of twelve He was taken to Jerusalem for His Bar-Mitzvah, just like any other boy reaching what was then called manhood. He may then have learnt to be a carpenter and to help in His father's workshop. It is further assumed that Joseph died and that Jesus, now the man of the family, took over the family business caring for His brothers and sisters and Mary His mother.

It seems likely that John, the cousin of Jesus, may well have been orphaned at an early age and been taken to a monastery, perhaps the Qumran Community, in the wilderness by the Dead Sea, and brought up by The Essenes. At some particular time he felt God calling him to leave the monastery and begin a preaching mission. Apparently he made quite an impact on his congregations, for news of his preaching as well as his appearance spread around the region.

People were eager to hear his words about the coming Messiah. When Jesus, who was now about thirty years old, heard the news about John, He too knew that this was the time to begin His ministry.

So Jesus left home, presumably with His eldest brother James now in charge of the business, and set off to find John, already nicknamed 'The Baptist'. He may have taken the road from Nazareth to Scythopolis and on to Aenon near Salim and the River Jordan. Imagine, if you will, Jesus looking down from the hillside to the river below. He sees John standing in the river, baptising all those who have responded to his call to repentance and who want to make a new start to their lives. Jesus sets off down the dusty track to the river bank.

PART ONE

FROM

THE RIVER JORDAN

TO

CAESAREA PHILIPPI

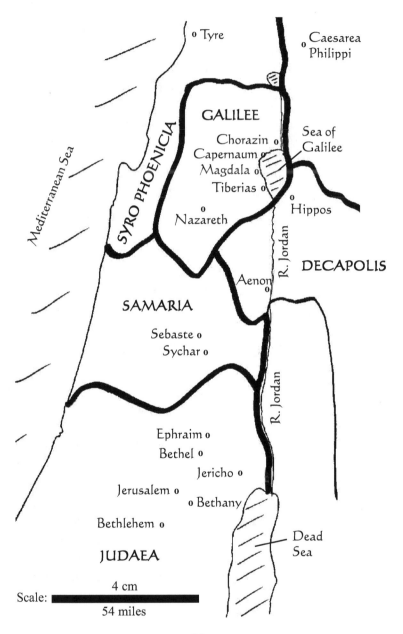

CHAPTER 1

His Baptism and the
Challenge of the Temptations

WHEN Jesus reached the river bank, He stepped into the water and joined the queue of people waiting to be baptised. Soon it was His turn. In front of Him, John scooped up handfuls of water ready for the next person. He began to pray aloud for a blessing when he looked up and into the eyes of Jesus. After a moment's hesitation he realised who it was in front of him, and stopped what he was doing.

Without any formal greeting, he said to Jesus, 'You should be baptising me'.

'No,' Jesus replied, 'for this is indeed a new beginning to my life,' and He knelt down in the water. So John baptised Jesus and asked God's blessing on Him and His ministry.

Though Jesus, at home in Nazareth, had prepared for His ministry and waited for the moment when it would begin, He now felt guided to go into the wilderness to be alone, to fast and to pray. He needed time to meditate on what principles His ministry should be based. At one point He became very hungry. He looked at a nearby stone. He knew that He had the power to turn that stone into bread and thus satisfy His hunger. He resisted the temptation, and in doing so decided that this was not the right use of His power. In terms of His ministry,

He must not use such power to draw crowds and then influence them by giving them all the physical things they needed.

Perhaps later, because He was tired and it was at the hottest time of the day, He was lost in thought or dreaming. Perhaps He thought for a moment He could see the dome of the Temple glinting in the sunshine. He imagined that He was standing on the pinnacle of that Temple in Jerusalem. There were crowds below wondering if this was someone about to commit suicide. 'Go on', someone seemed to be shouting, 'Jump! You'll be all right. Your Father would not let you die. He will see to it that you do not hurt yourself. Think how impressed everyone will be when they see you pick yourself up and walk away.' Once again Jesus knew that He had to resist such a temptation. This was not the way to encourage faith, to get people to believe in Him. He would not use the miraculous to convert people to His way of living.

Jesus got up, stretched himself, and continued His walk through the wilderness. He climbed one of the highest peaks on the nearby hills, sat down, and looked on the valleys below and the distant scene. Once again it was as if there were voices in His mind. 'Take the easy way,' they seemed to be saying. 'Do not go about preaching threats of God's punishment on all those who break His laws. People don't like that. Be prepared to compromise. Let them enjoy their sinful pleasures. Your ministry will be so much easier!' Jesus stood up. 'No. No. No!' He exclaimed aloud. 'There is only one way, and that is the way of honesty and integrity. I will not compromise with truth. I will not be tempted in this way!' At last He knew that His struggle with temptation, at this point in His life at least, was over. He had met His first challenge. Now He was ready to begin.

CHAPTER 2

Capernaum

JESUS walked up the river valley, following the road that many Galilean pilgrims did, along the East bank of the Jordan, thus avoiding going through Samaria. He probably travelled through the region of Decapolis, crossing the river Jordan and on to the town of Scythopolis. Here He would have turned north, walking over the hills behind Tiberias, down Mount Arbel and on to the north coast of Lake Galilee. The town of Tiberias was placed out of bounds to all Jews by the Sanhedrin because it had been built by Herod Antipas on the site of a graveyard. He then came to the lakeside town of Capernaum. On the Sabbath day He went into the local synagogue in order to attend the usual act of worship and teaching. Members of the congregation not only noticed that they had a visitor but that He was dressed in a white seamless garment which gave Him the appearance of a Teacher. Jesus shared in the reading of the psalms as each group of men on either side of the synagogue repeated well-known verses.

'The earth is the Lord's and all that is in it,' one group proclaimed.

'The world and all who live within it,' came the reply.

And later, 'Lift up your heads Oh ye gates; be lifted up

ye ancient doors, that the King of glory might come in'.

'Who is this King of Glory?' came the question as a response. Jesus wondered if they would in time recognise who He really was.

When the Leader of the synagogue reached that point in the service where someone is asked to give their understanding and interpretation of the Scripture, he invited Jesus to sit in the Seat of Moses, a place reserved in every synagogue for the preacher. He then instructed the attendant to pass the scroll to Jesus. So Jesus preached His first sermon. It was so effective that He was asked to return. The people were amazed at the way He spoke, for there was a simplicity and yet an authority in His words. He seemed to know what was right and wrong, as opposed to other preachers who spent most of their time quoting other rabbis.

On another Sabbath day, Jesus had again been preaching in the synagogue, when a man in the congregation had a fit. He started shouting at Jesus, 'Go away, go away! We want nothing to do with You Jesus from Nazareth! You have come here to destroy us! I know you!'

Jesus immediately took control of the situation. He held the man firmly with His hands and looked straight into his eyes. 'Be quiet!' He said forcibly. Immediately the man began to relax. 'Be at peace,' Jesus continued, this time speaking gently. To the surprise and amazement of the congregation, the man first of all lost consciousness, lay on the ground, then recovered and was all right again.

Those who had witnessed what had happened, said, 'What is it about this man? Not only are His words powerful as a preacher, but also as a healer!' Needless to say, the story of what had happened that day spread throughout the town and the neighbouring villages like wildfire.

Some fishermen, from Bethsaida, a fishing village on the other side of Lake Galilee, had come ashore the following day in order to sell their fish in Capernaum. They soon heard the news, and Andrew took time off to find Jesus in order to listen to His preaching and teaching. He was bowled over by what he heard and saw. Jesus was challenging everyone to turn away from their sinful ways, to turn again to God, in order to get to know God better, and He promised them that The Kingdom of God was very near.

When Andrew returned to his boat, he told his brother Peter, 'I have met the Messiah!'

Philip, a fisherman in another boat, also from Bethsaida, decided to go and listen to Jesus as well. He too was so impressed that he went back to the boat to tell his partner Nathaniel. 'I have met the Messiah,' he said. 'His name is Jesus and He comes from Nazareth.'

'Can anything good come out of Nazareth?' Nathaniel said sarcastically.

'Just come and see for yourself,' Philip replied.

Nathaniel reluctantly agreed. As they were walking in the direction where the crowds had been, Jesus came towards them. 'Now here is a man of deep thought and integrity,' Jesus said, looking straight at Nathaniel. Nathaniel was completely taken aback, for Jesus spoke as if He already knew him. 'I saw you once, praying while sitting in the shade of a fig tree,' Jesus explained. After he had spent some time with Jesus, Nathaniel also accepted that Jesus really was the Messiah.

On another occasion, Jesus was preaching down by the shore of the Lake. People had gathered to buy fish from the fishermen who had just landed their catch. The fishermen were obviously dispirited for there were very few fish to sell. Jesus grasped the opportunity and began preaching, once more emphasising His challenge for people to make a new start to their lives. As word got round that Jesus was preaching down by the lakeside, more and more people gathered. In fact, the crowds were so large that Jesus was nearly forced into the water. He noticed two empty boats on the beach and asked their owners if He could use one of them, to push out onto the edge of the lake and then preach from the boat. It so happened that the owner was Peter from Bethsaida. He was happy to accede to Jesus' request, pushed the boat into the water, helped Jesus into the boat and then, using the single paddle, manoeuvred the boat a short distance from the shore. Jesus continued His preaching, and Peter, sitting in the boat, listened to what He had to say.

When Jesus had finished, and the crowd began to wander back to their homes, He suggested to Peter that he should go fishing. Peter shook his head. 'We were fishing all night and caught nothing'. However, there was something in the eyes of Jesus which made him feel in the wrong. 'All right,' he said reluctantly, 'we'll try again.' He paddled the boat back to the shore where Jesus got out, and Andrew got in. They prepared the boat and the nets and set off from the shore.

Not far out, they released their nets carefully overboard and began to trawl for fish. Almost immediately their nets were slowing the boat down because of the weight of the fish in them. So much so in fact that Peter shouted to James and John, their partners in another boat, to come out in their boat to help them. They did so, and within a short time both boats were so full of fish that they were on the point of sinking! They rowed back to the shore pulling their nets behind them. Peter was amazed at what had happened.

'How on earth did He know?' he asked Andrew.

'I told you He was the Messiah,' Andrew replied, and smiled with satisfaction.

When they reached the shore once more, they pulled their boats onto the beach as far as they would go.

Peter was quite overcome by the sight of all the fish. When Jesus came towards him he fell to his knees in front of Jesus. Tears were not very far away when he said, 'Sir, please leave me. I am not worthy enough for Your being here.'

Jesus put His hand on Peter's head. 'Don't worry. From now on, you and I will be fishing for men!'

News of the catch of fish soon brought the customers back to the shore. When all the fish had been sold and the people had gone home, the four fishermen tidied their boats and folded their nets. Jesus was sitting down nearby.

Peter called to Him. 'Where are you staying tonight?'

Jesus replied, 'Foxes have holes, and birds have their nests, but I have no home here.'

'Then you will come and stay with us,' Peter said as if he were giving an order to his crew. When they had finished their work, Peter, Andrew, Philip, and Nathaniel, together with Zebedee and his two sons James and John, went to Peter's home and he invited others to come and listen to Jesus.

That evening, Jesus was more formally introduced to the fisherman called Zebedee and his two sons James and John, another fishing family from Bethsaida. They talked most of the night, and in the morning the two sons asked to stay with Jesus as if they were students of a rabbi.

Jesus stayed with Peter and his family for a few days. News of Jesus and His preaching, the healing of the man with the fit and other stories, had already spread throughout the town. On the next Sabbath day, Jesus was asked to preach in the synagogue. Afterwards, when everyone was coming out of the synagogue, Peter's wife was waiting for them, looking very anxious.

'What's the matter, dear?' asked Peter.

'It's my mother,' his wife replied. 'She's been taken ill and is in bed with some sort of fever.' They all hurried back to Peter's house. Peter went immediately to the sleeping area and knelt beside his mother-in-law. Then after a few moments he got up and made way for Jesus. Jesus came forward, knelt beside the bed and held the woman's hand. He prayed with her, talked to her, and very soon she seemed to be at peace. Later, when the family were having their meal, they were amazed to see the same woman, not only up and on her feet but helping her daughter with the food for the meal. People who had seen Peter's wife and knew of the sudden illness of her mother called at the house to ask how she was. When they saw her and heard what had happened, they could not wait to tell everyone else the news.

At sunset, before Jesus and the family had finished their meal, a crowd of people had gathered in the street outside the house asking for Jesus. Many of them were ill or had brought friends or family members who were ill. Jesus came out to them, talked with each one, prayed with them and laid His hands on them. Many people found peace of mind. They had been healed from their fears and phobias, their fits and their anxieties. It was very late by the time He had finished and everyone had gone home.

First thing in the morning, in fact before daybreak, Jesus got up, went out of the town, walked some way into the wilderness to be on His own to pray. Later that morning, Peter and Andrew came looking for Him. When they found Him, they said, 'Everyone is asking for You. Please come back to town.'

Jesus replied, 'This is only the beginning. We must go on to other towns as well so that I can pass on to all the people of the region the Good News of God.' Jesus went back with them and ministered to the needs of the people.

So Jesus began His ministry, preaching, teaching and healing, in the province of Galilee. Peter, Andrew, Philip, Nathaniel, James, and John went with Him. During the next few months they travelled around the Lake stopping at each of the towns and villages, passing through Capernaum, Magdala, even Tiberias, and Cana on their way to Nazareth, Jesus's home town.

One day, when they were out in the wilderness, they came across a leper. When the man saw them he came towards them. The disciples stepped back, afraid of the disease, but Jesus stood where He was. The leper came and knelt near to Jesus.

'I have heard about you,' he said. 'You can heal me if you want to,' he added pleadingly.

Jesus, moved with pity for the man, took a step forward, stretched out His hand and placed it on the head of the leper. His followers held their breath. 'I want to,' Jesus said, 'be healed!'

The man felt Jesus's hands on his head, and his eyes filled with tears. It had been so long since someone had touched him.

Jesus continued, 'You will find that your illness is now in remission. When you are cured and the sores have healed, go into the nearest town and let yourself be examined by the authorities in order to be declared 'clean'. Then go to the synagogue and give thanks to God in the traditional way for what He has done for you. Do it quietly so that people do not panic and cause you more problems.'

However, when the man found that indeed he was cured, he was so excited that he ran to the nearest town and told everyone he saw what had happened and how Jesus had healed him. So the stories and rumours about Jesus spread quickly around the whole province, and, everywhere Jesus went, crowds of people were waiting for Him, especially those who were ill.

CHAPTER 3

Nazareth

HAVING lived almost all His life in Nazareth, it seemed strange to Jesus to come back to His home town, not as 'the carpenter's son' but as a man with a reputation, and with a group of men with Him who were happy to be called His disciples. He made straight for His home and introduced His friends to His mother, His brothers, and His sisters. There was a little time to relax before news of His return spread around the town.

The first moment of real challenge came on the Sabbath day. Jesus and His disciples went to the synagogue, as He always did, and, of course, the place was full and there was an excited attitude and atmosphere. The whispers could easily be heard.

'Isn't that the carpenter's son, Joseph's boy?'

'I can remember Him when He used to play with my sons!'

Everyone there had already heard about Jesus and His preaching, and it came as no great surprise when the leader of the synagogue instructed the attendant to give the scroll to Jesus to read the scripture and then to preach about it. The scripture chosen for that day was from the prophet Isaiah. Jesus began to read. 'The spirit of the Lord God is upon me; He has appointed me to preach the Good News to the poor; He has sent me to heal the broken-hearted, to announce that political prisoners will be set free, the blind shall once more see and those who are servants and slaves will be released from their subjection. God is ready to give His blessing to all those who come to know Him and offer their whole selves to Him.'

It was a clear prophecy about the Messiah. Jesus rolled up the scroll, gave it back to the attendant, and waited for him to return the scroll to its proper place. All eyes were on Jesus. 'Today,' said Jesus slowly, 'this scripture has come true.'

There was a short silence while His words sank in. Then there were gasps and suddenly an uproar!

'Blasphemy!' shouted one of the leaders of the synagogue.

'How dare you!' shouted another, and many men were shaking their fists in anger.

'You cannot be the Messiah' said another. 'You're from our town. We know you, we knew your mother and your father before you. You cannot be the Messiah. This is outrageous!'

Some of the men did try to get the rest to be quiet so that Jesus could answer their accusations but they could not make themselves heard. Some started to leave the synagogue in protest, some shouted abuse as they left, while others tried to restore some sort of order and dignity.

When it was a little quieter, someone shouted out, 'Perform one of Your miracles, then we might believe you!'

'No,' said Jesus, 'that is the wrong use of My power. That is not the right path to true faith.' By now more people had left the synagogue, but also more people inside were listening to what Jesus had to say. 'The old adage is still true, that "a prophet is not accepted in his own home territory". Remember Elijah? He helped the woman from Zarepath, a foreigner, when there were plenty of other Jewish widows in need because of the terrible drought that existed. And what about Elisha, another prophet, who healed a foreigner, Naaman, when there were plenty of Jewish lepers in need of healing? People said, "This cannot be the work of God because foreigners were being helped and healed." As long as people are bound up with tradition and nationalism, they will never be able to see God at work in any other way. So also with the concept of Messiah. I do not fit in with your ideas so you assume that I cannot be the Messiah. The Good News of God is already being accepted by people that your society has rejected. I tell you plainly, even some prostitutes, collaborators, and foreigners will reach heaven before you, because they have believed in me.'

Any tacit support that Jesus had had up to that moment disappeared with those last words.

'Get Him out' some shouted. 'He has defiled our synagogue.' And they jostled Jesus so that He was forced to leave the building. Outside it was soon obvious that a mob had formed, and the disciples were afraid for Jesus and for themselves. No-one actually man-handled Jesus, but He was nevertheless forced to walk along the road, out of the town, that led to the cliff. He had walked that way many times before. The threat was obvious. His life was in danger. As the crowd moved towards the cliff, the volume of noise subsided. It was the Sabbath, and only now were they remembering that fact.

By the time they reached the cliff, Jesus knew that their

aggression had diminished. Suddenly He turned round on them. They stopped in their tracks and were afraid of what He might do. All He did however, was to walk through the crowd, for they parted as He moved towards them.

The disciples eventually caught up with Jesus. 'Now you know what to expect,' Jesus said. They walked back to the town, and back to His home. He stayed several days at home before continuing His ministry in the neighbouring villages.

CHAPTER 4

The Hole in the Roof

SEVERAL weeks later, Jesus and His group of disciples returned to Capernaum. There were now other people, many of whom were women, who travelled with them, gladly taking on the roll of providers. Jesus had not invited them, but they seemed happy to be able to help with regard to food, cooking meals, washing clothes and other minor needs. People in the towns and villages were only too pleased to give Jesus gifts of money, food, and refreshment, especially when He had healed a member of their family.

From time to time, Jesus was offered accommodation or invited to a meal, and on this occasion He had accepted. News of His return to the town spread quickly, and soon the house where Jesus was staying was besieged by people anxious to hear Him teach and preach, and once more many people were asking for healing, for themselves or their loved ones.

Four men arrived carrying their sick friend on a stretcher. He had been paralysed as the result of a fall. When they saw the crowds and realised that there was no way they were going to get in to see Jesus, one of them climbed the outside steps of the house onto the roof and examined it. He discovered that it was a typical beamed roof covered with tree branches and thick leaves in the centre. He came down again and then the four men carried their friend up the steps onto the roof. They laid their friend down and started pulling away the leaves and the branches. When they had made a large enough hole in the roof they tied their tie belts onto each handle of the stretcher and lowered their friend down into the room below.

Meanwhile, when bits of leaves, roofing and dust started falling down inside the house the people inside started to push backwards. They naturally created a space as they watched the stretcher being lowered. Jesus was impressed by the men's ingenuity and determination. He had been preaching about the forgiveness of God and the consequent peace of mind which in many cases led to a physical healing.

Now, unexpectedly, Jesus was presented with an actual challenge. After talking with the man on the stretcher to find out what had happened, and therefore learning a little about him, He prayed with the man and then laid His hands on him.

'As a result of your faith and that of your friends,' Jesus said to the man, 'your sins are forgiven. Go in peace.'

Immediately the Pharisees and other local Jewish leaders of the synagogue in the crowd were shocked. They whispered to one another, 'Only God can forgive sins. If this man is claiming to be God, then this is blasphemy and we should not be here! We should have nothing to do with Him.'

'I know what you are thinking,' Jesus said. 'You still do not know who I am, and you do not yet believe this connection between faith, the mind, and the body. Which do you think is the harder task, to forgive this man's sins or to heal his body?' He hesitated but, of course, there was no reply. 'I'll save you the problem of answering,' He continued. He bent down again over the man on the stretcher, took his hand and started to help him up. 'In the name of God you have been healed. Get up and go to your home.'

After a moment's hesitation, the man was amazed to find that he could get up, for his paralysis had gone. He got up, stretched himself, rolled up the stretcher, said, 'thank you' to Jesus and walked out of the house as the crowd parted, making a way for him to leave. He and his friends were so excited that they started to shout, and something of their excitement got through to the crowd. One person started to sing one of the psalms of David and it was not long before others joined in. However, the strict and orthodox Jews in the crowd were shocked and very unhappy, and shook their heads in disgust. All of them agreed though, as they walked home, that they had never seen anything like this in their lives.

Each day, Jesus walked through the town of Capernaum to the lakeside, and a crowd often gathered as He went along the roads. He taught, He answered questions, and He healed people. In the business section of the town, there was a table booth where everyone had to pay their taxes. The Roman occupation of Israel meant that everyone had to pay whatever was demanded. The army could not do everything so they recruited local people to help them in the area of administration. Those people who worked for the Romans, particularly in the collection of taxes, were treated as collaborators and hated by many within the community.

One day, Jesus was in that particular area of the town and He walked towards the tax booth. The official on duty that morning was named Matthew. Matthew guessed who

Jesus was because of His reputation, and looked up from his account books wondering what Jesus wanted. Jesus looked straight at Matthew.

'I want you to come and join me in my ministry,' Jesus said to him without any warning. Matthew was astonished. However, he was so filled with joy at the invitation, that he handed everything over to another official and went with Jesus. His natural reaction was to ask Jesus to his home for a meal and to meet his family including Alphaeus His father and his brother James.

Then, on the spur of the moment, he said, 'If I invite all my colleagues and friends to dinner this evening would you still come?'

'Yes, of course,' Jesus replied.

That evening, as usual, a crowd followed Jesus, hoping to hear Him preach and teach, and see Him heal those who were ill. When they realised where Jesus was going, and saw the sort of guests that had also been invited, some of the people in the crowd, those of a more strict religious opinion, were disdainful.

'How can He associate with such people? How can He eat and drink with such scum? There are plenty of other people who need His help,' they said.

Now Matthew, quite naturally, had invited his fellow administrators and others who had been ostracised by so-called 'decent' society. Such a meal was more like an open buffet that spread outside the house, rather than a meal in a room, so those who were not invited could still see and hear what was happening. Jesus was aware of the criticism of those who had not been invited. He looked at them and said, 'Sick people need a doctor. Those who are well do not. My message is for all who are spiritually sick and have need for God's love and are willing to listen to the call to repentance.'

Amongst those whom Jesus met that night was a man called Judas from Kerioth. He was a non-Jew and therefore not accepted in normal society. He was a leather-maker and trader. His appearance was unusual for he always wore a long leather coat with big pockets as an advertisement for his trade.

'Here's someone else who could help you, Jesus,' said Matthew jokingly. 'He could fill his big pockets with money for You!' Everyone laughed. Jesus just smiled. Later He talked with Judas and, what had started as a joke became a reality, for Jesus asked Judas to join his group of disciples and to act as treasurer while Matthew did the accounting. That same evening, Matthew's brother James asked to join the followers of Jesus.

By now, Jesus had decided that there would be an inner group of Disciples who would help Him with His ministry. As with most Rabbis of the day, Jesus knew that there would be a group of followers, and therefore there had to be some sort of organisation. He did not want to spend time on such matters, so men like Matthew and Judas would be invaluable. People came and went as they wished, and some times there were as many as one hundred and fifty people with Jesus. More often than not they would camp outside a town or village for the night.

At such times, Jesus began to train this inner group of followers, asking them questions, listening to their answers and their questions, and answering them with simple stories about everyday people and situations. On one Sabbath day, as this large group of people made their way from the nearby town and its synagogue, they were walking through a field of corn. Without thinking, many of them broke off ears of corn, rubbed them in their hands, blew away the chaff and ate the corn. Some of the religious leaders who had followed Jesus with the rest of the crowd, intending to listen to Him preach and teach, called to Jesus to stop His followers eating the corn.

'It is the Sabbath day,' they said. 'No one must harvest the corn on the Sabbath day for that is classed as work!'

Jesus turned on them. 'You know your scriptures,' He said. 'Do you remember when King David and his companions were hungry and they ate the bread from off the altar. That was against the Law as well but they were not arraigned as law breakers,' and He paused. 'The Law was designed to help people with their lives of faith and putting that faith into everyday practice, not to be a set of rules and regulations to be applied without understanding or exceptions.'

To back up their challenge, these men said, 'The disciples of John the Baptist fast. Why don't Your followers do the same thing?'

In reply, Jesus said, 'If you are invited to a wedding feast, do you refuse to eat and just sit there while others eat? Of course not! My disciples are rejoicing with me now as if I were the bridegroom. They do not need to fast.' Then, turning to the whole crowd of people, He said, 'Many of the old laws are now out of date and need replacing. Some of them cannot even be adapted to modern living. It would be like trying to put a new piece of leather on an old wine skin in order to repair a hole in it. When the new wine is poured in the result would be disastrous. The new leather would slowly expand and tear the rest of the skin apart and all the wine would be lost. No, new wine needs a new wine-skin. My message is like that new wine.'

On another occasion, two men from Tiberias were anxiously trying to find Jesus. They were disciples of John the Baptist and had come to tell Jesus of John's death. When they found Jesus they told Him their story.

Apparently, Herod had sent soldiers to arrest John. He had always been an outspoken critic of the King because of Herod's lavish life-style, his debauchery, and his violent injustice. This time he had been especially critical of his marriage to Herodias, his brother Philip's wife. He accused the king of adultery and sodomy. It was probably Herodias who was the driving force behind the arrest, for later she trapped Herod into having John beheaded.

There had been a private party, and Herodias had persuaded her daughter to dance for the guests. Herod was so pleased with her performance, and too drunk to realise what was going on, that he promised her, in front of his guests, anything she wanted as a reward. After talking with her mother, she asked for the head of John the Baptist. There was nothing Herod could do without losing face so he ordered John's execution. These two men, as well as others of John's disciples, had taken the body from the palace and given John a decent burial.

Jesus was sad to hear the news, and understood the violent feelings of the two men. 'In all humanity,' Jesus said, 'there was no-one with a greater faith. He is like the one to whom scripture referred, 'Look! I am sending a messenger ahead of you to prepare the way for you.'

'He was a fine disciplined man. He fasted regularly and never drank strong drink in his life. His preaching was fearless.

The world has lost a fine man.' Jesus thanked the two men for bringing Him the news. However, instead of leaving, the two men asked if they could join Jesus and His followers. Apparently John had told them to do this when he was in prison and realised that his life and work were over.

'John, our leader, said that he was not the bridegroom but the bridegroom's friend. He added that his influence on us must decrease, and yours should increase.' Jesus received them gladly. 'His influence on you must decrease but not his memory'. One was named Thaddeus and the other was named Simon, nicknamed 'the Zealot'. That night it was noticed that Simon and Judas were often in close conversation.

The last man to become one of the group of disciples, who later became known as The Twelve, was Thomas. He had been in the synagogue in Capernaum one Sabbath day when Jesus was there. He had heard much about Jesus and had come to see and hear Him for himself.

Some Pharisees were there and they had deliberately brought with them a man, whom they knew, who had a withered arm. They knew that Jesus would attend the synagogue that day and, seeing the man in need, would not be able to resist helping him. If Jesus did heal the man, then they had all the witnesses they needed to accuse and convict Jesus of breaking the law by working on the Sabbath. Healing was classed as work, so here the religious authorities would have an open and shut case.

When Jesus entered the synagogue, He not only saw the man with the withered arm straight away but realised that this was a deliberate trap. He did not hesitate, however, but went to the man, talked with him and prayed with him. Jesus and the man then faced the congregation. Jesus said to everyone, but particularly to the Pharisees in the congregation who had become the self-styled Rabbis of Judaism, 'Is it right to do good deeds on the Sabbath day? Is it a day to save a life or to destroy a life?' The Pharisees remained silent. This was not the time to use their seven rules of debate exploring the Biblical text amongst each other. Jesus continued, 'Do you expect people to take the text literally, or do you give them the freedom to interpret the text in an up-to-date situation?' Still they said nothing. Jesus was saddened by their deliberate silence and their obvious indifference to human need. He turned to the man and commanded, 'Stretch out your hand!'

The man looked disbelievingly at Jesus, but he seemed to gain in confidence by just looking at Jesus. In a few moments he began to feel a tingling sensation in his fingers. Slowly, but surely, he felt life coming into his withered arm. In front of that congregation, silent and yet tense with anticipation, he raised his arm, inch by inch, until it was stretched out in front. People gasped, and everyone knew that at any moment there would be an explosion of excitement. The Pharisees merely got up, left the synagogue with a gloating expression on their faces, and went immediately to the authorities. There they discussed plans as to how to remove Jesus, for it was obvious that He was a danger to them.

From Thomas's point of view, all his doubts had now disappeared. This man Jesus really was the Messiah, and he wanted to be part of His ministry. When the service had finished and the congregation had eventually left Jesus alone, Thomas approached Jesus. He asked Him if he might be allowed to become one of His disciples. Jesus welcomed him straight away and took him to meet the others.

Later that same day, Jesus and His disciples went down to the lakeside in order to travel by boat across the lake. Before He reached the boats, Jesus was surrounded by people who had come from all over the region, from the provinces of Judea and Idumea, as well as the towns of Tyre and Sidon. Some had travelled from the other side of the Jordan river and some had even come from Jerusalem.

Jesus was soon exhausted by such crowds and urged His disciples to have the boats ready so that they could all leave. At the end of the day He travelled with His disciples by boat while the other followers made their way round the lake. Jesus, having reached Bethsaida, once again went off on His own into the wilderness to pray and to relax after the day's exertions.

When He returned to their insula, a sort of camp site in a courtyard with branches overhanging one corner in order to provide shade, He gathered all His disciples together and announced who were to be His inner team, The Twelve. They were: Peter and Andrew, Philip and Nathaniel, James and John, Matthew, Judas, and James (Matthew's brother), Thaddaeus, Simon the Zealot, and Thomas.

CHAPTER 5

The Teacher

DURING the next few months, Jesus established His teaching ministry. One of the reasons why people were captivated by the teaching of Jesus was that He taught by means of stories about everyday life. Instead of lectures on the details of The Law, here was teaching which made religion interesting and meaningful. These are some of the stories that He told about farmers and the farming community.

'Once upon a time, a farmer went out into his fields to sow the seeds for next year's corn. As he scattered the seed by hand, some of it fell on the hard ground, the path trodden down by people walking past. The birds very quickly spotted it, flew down and ate it all up. Some of the seed fell into shallow ground particularly near the stony corners of the field. These seeds grew quickly, but when the new shoots came through they were exposed to the hot sun. Because the plants had little depth of soil they lacked nourishment, so they withered and died just as quickly.

Other seeds fell on the sides of the fields where thorn bushes and other weeds took root. When the new corn shoots came through, they were crowded out by the weeds and never amounted to anything. But the rest of the seed fell into good ground and produced a wonderful harvest, some plants with thirty ears of corn per head, some with sixty, and some with a hundred.'

Now most people readily understood His stories for they had seen this sort of thing happening. Their meaning, however, was not always obvious and there were times when these stories had to be made clear. For example, with this particular story about the farmer, Jesus explained, 'The farmer is God's messenger, and the seed is the Good News of God. There are those who, like the pathway, are hard-hearted and will not listen to the message. It is wasted on them. Then there are those who lead shallow lives. They respond immediately and with great enthusiasm. But as soon as their new way of life becomes difficult, as with persecution, they lose their enthusiasm and interest. The third category is like people who live crowded and busy lives. They too begin their new life with great enthusiasm but when they are forced to prioritise their time, selfish pleasure, the concern for money, and other interests take precedence and their new faith is forgotten.

However, there are those for whom their new faith is the greatest event of their lives, and they themselves grow in grace and become God's messengers and will tell many other people of the Good News with varying results. You need the right seed and the right soil, and then great things can be achieved.

On another occasion, Jesus was trying to inspire people with an understanding of the wonder of God's creation. 'Think of a farmer. He prepares the ground for his crop, sows the seeds, and then goes back to the farmhouse. The seeds grow, the plants begin to push through the ground without the farmer having to do anything. The plants continue to grow, thanks to the sun and the rain, and eventually the head is formed. First the leaves, then the chaff, and finally the corn inside. Only then does the farmer return with his sickle and harvest the corn. Isn't it wonderful what God our Father has done for us?'

Another similar story was that of the farmer and those who disliked him. It was a story about judgement. 'One day,' Jesus said, 'a farmer sowed his field with good seed. One night, while he was asleep, someone with a grudge against him sowed weed seeds in the same field. After some weeks, his workers noticed nothing unusual as they surveyed the young plants. However, after some months, when the good plants were beginning to produce their ears of wheat, his labourers noticed that there were weed heads, which are poisonous, all mixed up in the corn. They rushed to tell the farmer. "Sir," they said, "did you check the seed before you sowed your field?" "Yes," he replied. "Why do you ask?" "Well, we noticed today that there are thistles and other weeds growing amongst the corn plants." "I know who has done this," said the farmer who was now disappointed and annoyed. The labourers asked, "shall we go and pick out all the weeds?" "No," said the farmer, "because as you pick out the weeds you will tread on some corn plants or even pick some plants out as well. Leave them now until harvest. Then when we harvest the corn we will sort out the weeds and burn them, and then keep the good corn."'

The Pharisees were always quick to judge people and condemn them but they did not always realise the damage they were doing through their judgmental attitude. Jesus wanted them to realise that Judgement is the prerogative of God, not humanity.

Because Jesus always encouraged people to talk with Him and share their problems, He was familiar with the problems of their day. He would tell stories designed to help the people combat these difficulties. For example, there was the problem of envy.

'Once upon a time there was an owner of a large estate. When it came to the time of harvest he needed extra workers to help on the estate. First thing in the morning he went down to the town square where the unemployed waited to be hired. He hired all he could find and promised them a day's wage for a day's work. At midday, and again at three o'clock in the afternoon, he went to hire more men in order to get the harvesting finished. Finally, at five o'clock, he noticed more men hanging around. "Why aren't you working?" he asked the men. "Because no-one has hired us," they replied. "Then go and report to my foreman," the estate owner said, "and he will put you to work in my fields."

'At the end of the day, the owner called the workers into line in order to pay them their wages, beginning with the men who came last. Each man received a full day's wage! So when it was the turn of those who were hired earlier in the day, quite naturally they expected that they would be paid more. However, they too were paid for a full day's work. "That's not fair," they complained. "These men have only worked for a short period of time, whereas we have worked all day and through the heat of the day." The estate owner replied, "You agreed to work for a full day's wage and I have paid you what we agreed. If I choose to be generous, why should you complain? Is it against the Law to pay what I like to my workers? Should you be angry because I am generous? Be content with what you have and rejoice for the others."'

There were those who understood what Jesus was saying,

but some were on the side of the workers. 'We do not all have the same wealth in life,' continued Jesus. 'There are the rich and the poor. But we do all have the opportunity of coming to know God. If some come early in life... good for them. If others come later in life, then the important thing is that they have come to know God... not what happened to them beforehand. It may well be that the last shall be first, and the first shall be last coming into the Kingdom.'

Another story was about love and forgiveness.

'Once upon a time, a farmer had two sons. The younger son became dissatisfied with life on the farm and impatient for a more exciting way of living. One day he asked his father to give him, there and then, his half of his inheritance so that he could leave home and make a new start to his life. The father and his two sons worked out the value of the farm and then the farmer gave the younger son half of the value in money. The young man left home and travelled abroad. He was inexperienced in worldly ways, and his wealth soon attracted the attention of others. He organised parties, he gambled, he got drunk and spent money on prostitutes. It was not long before he had spent all his money. Suddenly there was a famine in that country and everyone suffered. He could not get proper employment, so in order to earn some money he took a job looking after pigs. He was paid so little and became so hungry that even the pig food looked appetising. He appealed to his new friends for help but now that he had no money they did not want to know him. At long last he came to his senses, realised that he had wasted his inheritance and made a mess of his life. "This is ridiculous," he said to himself. "Here I am starving to death, and at home even my father's servants have enough to eat. I will go home. I will say to my father, "Father, I have made a mess of my life and I can understand your being ashamed of me. I am no longer worthy of being called your son. So please will you employ me like one of your servants?"

'His father had never given up hope of his son's return, and one day word was brought to him that his son had been seen on his way home. He was thrilled and excited. He ran down the farm track to meet his son, flung his arms round him and kissed him. The son started to say his prepared speech. "Father, I realise that I am no longer worthy to be called your son..." but before he had time to complete it, his father had given orders for a feast to be prepared, for his son to be bathed and dressed in fine clothes, and for the neighbours to be invited to the welcome home party. "We will have a celebration," he said, "for this my son was lost and is found; he was dead and is alive again!" And so the preparations began.

'Meanwhile, the elder brother was working outside in the fields. When he returned to the farm he heard all the noise and saw all the preparations being made for the party. "What is going on?" he asked one of the servants. "Your brother has come home and your father is having a great feast to celebrate!" The elder brother was very angry and refused to attend the party. His father came to find him and begged him to come in and join them. "All these years I have worked for you," the elder son said. "I have always done what you wanted and yet you never gave me a party. But as soon as this brother of mine comes home, presumably having frittered away half your wealth on drink and debauchery, you throw him a party. It's not fair!" "Son," replied the father, "you are always with me, and everything I have is yours. But it is right to celebrate. This, your brother, whom we thought was dead, is alive; he was lost and is found! Please come and celebrate with us.'"

Jesus wanted them all to realise that anyone who comes to know God, is loved and forgiven by God, and we should therefore celebrate that fact. Coming to know God, at whatever stage in life, is more important than how many years we have known Him, and how faithful we have been to God.

There were times when, with people following Him wherever He went, Jesus used the opportunity for particular teaching sessions as well as question and answer sessions like the Rabbis. For example, there was one occasion when Jesus and the disciples had walked up one of the tiny valleys formed by one of the streams running into the Lake of Galilee, between Capernaum and Magdala. Jesus and the disciples were sitting on a flat area of land while those who were following sat down on the valley sides where they could see and hear clearly.

Jesus addressed them with the usual words of greeting, 'Peace be with you,' and the crowd replied, 'and also with you'.

'There are times,' He began, 'when our experiences of life give us the impression that so much in life is unfair or unjust. The rich have power because they can buy position and control the situation. They can influence the judges, buy their way out of trouble, afford anything they want. You might well say, "If you have not got money, you have not got a hope." However, it may be that you have got things the wrong way round. These are not the people that you should envy. Sometimes the unhappiest people could be the happiest.

'For example, there are those who mourn and are devastated by the loss of a loved one. These can be the happiest people on earth when they learn to look away from their own selfish loss, however natural, and see the gain of their loved one who now lives in heaven with God. They can have great joy.

'There are other people for whom you feel sorry. Think about those who seem rather pathetic for they have so little spirit. They allow themselves to be treated badly without fighting back; they have nothing and no one to help them rise out of their situation. Yet the Kingdom of Heaven will be given to them and they will have great joy, for those whom you see as poor in spirit are better able to appreciate what matters most in life, and can enjoy the wonder of spiritual things.

'Those who have nothing, who have to be humbly grateful to everyone for anything that they receive, will one day find happiness because they will be rich in spiritual things. The whole world will be theirs, for such people are truly grateful for anything that God gives them.

'Those who suffer from injustice because of the rich and powerful but who recognise what is wrong with society and long for God's rule to be established, will one day be rewarded by seeing His righteousness at work in the world, and they will then know joy.

'Those who show kindness and are unbiased in their attitude to other people in spite of the merciless prejudice that is around them will receive great joy in experiencing God's loving mercy for themselves.

'Those whose hearts and minds remain pure in the polluted society in which they live will know real bliss for they will truly be able to see God at work in themselves.

'Those who accept the role as peace-makers will soon know what a thankless task it can be. However, they will receive as their reward the greatest peace that there can be, peace of mind, because this is God's peace.

'Those who are mocked and sidelined because they are good people, rejected by society because of their moral standards, will have the joy of knowing that God is with them every moment of every day.

'If you find that people jeer at you, persecute you, and tell lies about you because you have become one of my followers, then be glad. You will receive a great reward from God because you have come to know Him, you love Him and you want to serve Him. Remember there are those who persecuted the prophets all those years ago. The prophets are remembered and their words honoured but their persecutors are long since forgotten.

'But no-one cares about us,' shouted a man from the crowd. 'We are treated as rubbish by the Romans, the rich and powerful that you have been talking about, and even our own religious leaders!'

'No,' replied Jesus. 'You are the salt of the earth. You matter to God. But just as salt has got to retain its sharpness in order to add taste to food that is bland, or to preserve what is needed to last, so you must see that your presence and needs are noticed and known by the authorities to maintain the true flavour of society and to re-establish God's authority.' He paused and then continued. 'You need to be like a light. At night time you do not put the light under a bowl to hide it, but you put it on a lamp-stand for everyone to be able to see what they are doing. Similarly, if you are travelling at night, you know that a city which is built on a hill cannot be missed. You see it from quite a distance because of the lights shining in the darkness. Now you must be seen and help others to see what God wants so that in time everyone will be able to praise and thank God for who He is and what He has done.'

Someone else in the crowd asked, 'Master, there are those Scribes and Pharisees who claim that you have no respect for the Law, that You do what You please. Is this true and is it all right for us to do the same?'

'No', replied Jesus, 'I have not come to get rid of the Law or the guidance of the Prophets. I have come to remind people of the true spirit and purpose that lie behind the Law and to fulfil the vision of the Prophets. The Law has lasted for many centuries and it will last to the end of time itself. Neither will it change in its significance. If you are faithful to the Law and obey the spirit of the Law, which sets out what God requires of you; if you teach people to have the same attitude and respect that you have, then God will be faithful to you and respect you and your needs.'

'But what do you mean by "the spirit behind the law"? another man asked. 'We have been taught the details of the Law but not the spirit of the Law.'

Jesus looked round at the crowd. 'You know that the Law says, "It is a crime to commit murder. Anyone who kills someone else will be brought to court and punished accordingly." But I tell you this, if you are angry and have violent thoughts and words about someone else, God will judge you for that. It is not just the action that is wrong but what lies behind it. God wants you to be under self-control and then there will be no more violence.'

'It is like your act of worship,' Jesus went on. 'If you come to the synagogue with your thanksgiving offering thanking God for His gifts of Peace and Joy and yet you have had a row with your brother, first of all leave your gift there, go to your brother and make your peace with him.

Then come back to the synagogue and your gift will now have the added blessing of sincerity.'

'Likewise,' He continued, 'suppose someone threatens to take you to court because of your violence. Settle the matter out of court. Apologise and make some sort of compensation. If you are arrested and go to court you will be found guilty, sent to prison and left there until your fine or its equivalent has been paid. But think of the time that you have wasted and the further problems that you have caused for your family. So do not become violent. It pays to be a man of peace.'

An older man got to his feet and asked, 'what about the Laws concerning adultery and divorce?'

Jesus responded, 'The Law clearly states "Do not commit adultery." However I would say this. Any man who looks at a woman who is not his wife and has fantasies about making love to her has already committed adultery in his heart and mind, and is therefore just as guilty. If every man were pure and faithful then there would be less likelihood of such immorality. With regard to divorce,' Jesus went on, 'anyone who divorces his wife just because he wants a change, and not because she has been unfaithful to him, not only makes her an adulteress if she marries again but he himself is just as guilty of adultery when he marries again.'

There were murmurs in the crowd as they listened. 'The important consideration here is the promise that has been made, whether it is in the context of marriage or anything else,' Jesus said. 'If you make a vow in the name of God, then you must keep it, whatever the circumstances. Adding a phrase like, "by the hairs of my head", or, "on my mother's grave", adds nothing to the sincerity of the vow. If you say

"Yes, I will", or, "No, I will not", then that should be sufficient. Your word is your bond.'

'Teacher,' called out another man from those sitting on the hillside. 'You teach and preach about Love. But we are an occupied country with foreigners telling us what to do. These people, and those who work for them, abuse us. How can we love other people under these circumstances?'

Jesus understood what lay behind the question. 'You know that the Law states that justice means "an eye for an eye" and "a tooth for a tooth". The punishment must be equivalent to the crime. But I say to you, do not take matters into your own hands. Bitterness and revenge will only produce more violence. If someone slaps you on one cheek, do not slap him back but turn your other cheek for him to hit if he dares. Retaliation serves no purpose at all, and in fact will only get you into worse trouble. Similarly, if someone is so petty-minded as to sue you in the courts for something as insignificant as your shirt, then give him your coat as well. If a Roman soldier commandeers you to carry his pack for a mile, do not retaliate and complain about the injustice of his request, but carry it two miles instead. You will achieve far greater personal peace through this loving attitude than by any violent response.'

Jesus was sympathetic to their needs and said, 'The Law says, "Love your friends and hate your enemies". However, I say to you, "Love your enemies and be prayerfully concerned about those who persecute you". Everyone matters equally to God. Just as the sun shines on the good and the bad, so the rain falls on the righteous and the unrighteous. God is not going to give you a special blessing because you love the people who already love you. That is easy. Even the so-called collaborators can do that. The hard thing to do is to love those who hate you and abuse you.' Jesus concluded this answer by saying 'God wants you to be like Him, to be perfect. Now that is the challenge. You will not achieve it by just keeping the Law. You can achieve it by working with God in keeping the spirit of the Law.' This was greeted with silence. Jesus seemed to be asking too much of everyone.

There were a number of Pharisees in the crowd, and one of them took advantage of the silence. 'Rabbi,' he asked, 'you already have a reputation for attending the synagogue regularly on the Sabbath and thus keeping the Law. Yet you also have a reputation for breaking the laws about the Sabbath. What are we to do? Follow your example?' He sat down feeling pleased with himself.

Jesus knew the hypocrisy that lay behind the question and was well aware of the danger that existed if He challenged the questioner directly. 'Make sure that you perform your public duties as the Law requires, including the laws about the Sabbath Day. But when you perform your private duties, do so discreetly and genuinely. If you are being charitable, do not make a show of it so that everyone can see what you are doing. Help whoever it is in private, for God, who has prompted your charitable giving, sees whatever is done in private and will then reward you.'

Once again, addressing the crowd rather then the individual questioner, Jesus said, 'When you pray to God, do not stand on street corners trying to impress every passer-by with your devotional commitment. No, go into some quiet corner of your house, and talk quietly with God. He knows where you are and hears every word and perceives every thought. Similarly, when you pray, do not use clichés and meaningless words just because they sound right. Do not think for a moment that God is going to be impressed by long prayers either.'

'So teach us how to pray,' said one of the disciples sitting near Jesus.

'All right,' replied Jesus. 'When you pray, get the right balance between your praise of God and your asking Him for help. For example, you might pray: "O God, My Father in Heaven, I honour You and worship You. May your heavenly Kingdom be established on earth as in heaven. May everyone do Your will. Please give us sufficient food and refreshment, the necessities of life, in order to live our lives. Forgive the mistakes that we have made and help us to forgive those who have wronged us. Give us the strength to resist temptation when it comes so that we can become the person that You want us to be."'

'Thank you,' said one of the other disciples, 'but why should we forgive other people when they are the ones in the wrong?'

Jesus answered him by saying, 'if you forgive them, even though they have wronged you, then you will be better able to appreciate what you are asking of God. You want Him to forgive you because you want to have a perfect loving relationship with God. He wants you to have a loving relationship with everyone else. So learn to love and forgive.'

Another Pharisee wanted to bring the teaching back to the subject of obedience to the Law. 'The Law states that we should fast. Do You think that this is right for all of us?' and he looked straight at the Twelve.

'Yes,' replied Jesus, 'but the point of fasting is about

self-discipline. Do not pretend to be holy and give the impression that your fasting is an illustration of the depth of your devotion. Neglecting your appearance, looking pale, and throwing dust all over yourself, to impress people as they pass you by standing on the street corners, will not impress God. This is hypocrisy! God knows who you are and what are the real motives behind all that you do and say. Whatever your form of devotion takes, make sure that it is genuine and in private. God who sees and hears everything will reward your sincerity.'

Jesus had silenced the questioner, but He went on, 'What you see and dwell on affects what you are and what you do. Your eye, like the light from a lamp, sees so much. If your eye concentrates on what is good and pure in life, then your body will be good and pure and it will be full of light. But if your eye concentrates on the darker side of life, then little light will enter in and your body will be in darkness. Then your words and deeds will be evil, reflecting the darkness in your true self.'

'Teacher,' said another man, standing up from the crowd on the hillsides, 'you tell us that it does not matter that we are poor. But because we are poor we are vulnerable. We are worried whether we shall have enough to eat, whether there will be any work in order to earn money for food and clothing, whether we can pay the Roman taxes.' He sat down but there were murmurs of approval and agreement.

Jesus replied, 'I do understand your problem. I have had to run a family carpentry business. However, I also know that the need for money can quickly become the love of money and that can become an addiction. No slave can work for two masters. He will be faithful to one and neglect the other, or vice versa. Now your responsibility is to serve God.

Beware of the danger of the love of money.'

As if this last remark had been an introduction to a sermon, Jesus continued, 'Do not worry about money, or food or clothes. Think about life itself. Isn't that wonderful? Look at the birds flying around. They do not work for their living. They do not sow seed and harvest the corn. But God provides for all their needs. If you worry about these things, will that help you to live longer and thus appreciate life more? No, of course not! Look at the flowers on the hillside around you. They do not sew cloth or weave garments. Yet Solomon in all his glory was not dressed as beautifully as these hillsides in summertime. So do not worry. You are meant to be people of faith. Therefore, put your faith into action. Trust God to look after you. Do not start worrying about tomorrow and what the day will bring. Learn to live each day and then you will be better able to take care of tomorrow.'

'Ask God for what you need,' Jesus said, 'for like any father He will answer you. Ask and you will receive; seek and you will find, knock at the door and He will answer you. If your son knocked at your door and asked for some bread, would you give him a stone? If he asked for fish, would you give him a snake? If you, being the imperfect people that you are, know how to give good gifts to your loved ones, surely you can understand and trust that God, who is perfect, will give you what you need?'

One man, on the edge of the crowd, who might well have been a judge, asked Jesus, 'If you say that we must abide by the spirit of the Law, rather than the detail of the Law, how can anyone make a judgement about another person?'

Jesus answered by saying, 'Do not sit in judgement on

other people. There is only one person who can sit in judgement and that is God, for He is the only one who knows everything there is about everyone. While we are sitting in judgement on other people, He is sitting in judgement on us! Similarly, how can you sit in judgement on your brother, pointing out his crime which is like a speck of dust compared with your crimes which seem like a plank of wood? First of all, get your own life in order and free from mistakes before you dare to point out the mistakes of others. Set the right example. Treat people in the way that you would want them to treat you. It is much harder to be good and to maintain high moral standards. It is so much easier to give into temptation and let evil have its way. It is like the fully laden camel approaching the gate of the city. The centre arch is broad and easy for the camel. But can you imagine the struggle to get it in through the pedestrian gate at the side if the main gate is shut? Most people sadly go through the wide gate of life because it is the easier way.'

There were plenty of smiles at this illustration. 'Lord,' asked a Pharisee, 'how do we know that what you say is right?'

'Not everyone who calls me "Lord",' Jesus responded, 'is automatically welcomed into the Kingdom of Heaven.' And again turning to the crowd said, 'You do not throw Holy food to the dogs. They will not appreciate it, but just demand more. Similarly, it is no good offering pearls to pigs. All they will do is to trample them in the mud. Be on your guard for false teachers and prophets. They may seem to be genuine but some are like wolves with a sheep's skin draped over them. Watch them carefully and you will be able to decide for yourself by the way they act. You cannot get grapes from thorn bushes, and you certainly cannot get figs from brambles. By their fruit, what they produce, you will know who and what they are.'

Jesus came to the end of this teaching session when He told this story. 'If you believe Me and trust in My words then you will be like a man who decided to build a house by the lakeside. He rightly chose to build on rock for his foundations. When the storms came, the wind and rain buffeted the house. It stood the strain and survived. However, if you choose not to believe me, then you will be like another man who built his house on the easier sandy base which required less work. However, when the storms came and the wind and rain buffeted the house, it collapsed and fell down, for the foundations were insufficient to stand the strain. The choice is yours,' Jesus concluded.

When Jesus had finished His teaching session, people talked with one another. They were amazed at the way He taught. It was so interesting, so down to earth, and when He spoke He seemed to have an authority which gave you the feeling that He was right.

By now, more and more people had joined the crowd. It always amazed the disciples how word about Jesus and His whereabouts travelled so quickly. Many sick people had formed a sort of queue, waiting for Jesus to begin a healing session. Mixed in with this particular part of the crowd in the narrow valley, were some children. Naturally enough, they squirmed their way to the front. Some of The Twelve were quick to their feet to stop them getting in the way. Jesus saw what they were doing and stopped them immediately. 'Let them all come,' He shouted to the disciples. They came and stood around Jesus. He talked with them, and then, one by one, He laid His hands on them and blessed them. Afterwards He picked up one child and sat him on His knees. He motioned for the crowd to be quiet. 'Unless you accept me like these little children, you will not be able to enter the Kingdom of God. In their innocence they trust me and will do as I say.' After a short time, He put the boy down and told the children to leave Him. Then He began His healing session. As He talked with each one, He found that they had come from all over the area, even as far as Tyre and Sidon.

Later in the day, He began His next teaching session with another series of stories and illustrations. He began by asking a rhetorical question. 'How can I describe the Kingdom of God? I could tell you its value. There was once a merchant who dealt in fine pearls. Everywhere he went he bought and sold pearls, looking for the very finest that there was. When he found what he believed to be the finest he had ever seen, he sold all his other pearls in order to purchase that one pearl. The Kingdom of God is like that one pearl.'

Jesus knew that the people loved His stories, so He continued. 'Once upon a time, a wealthy merchant held a grand party to mark the engagement in marriage of His daughter. Family and friends had been invited to stay at his large estate. In the evening, when the party was in full swing in the square forming the centre of the house, around the garden and the fountain, some thieves climbed up the outer walls and broke into the guests' rooms through the roof. As they were leaving, walking along the roof, someone saw them, and the men all started to chase after them. It was dark and the thieves were slowed down by the bags of money and jewels that they had stolen. They decided to bury their bags in the ground and come back later.'

'Some years later,' Jesus continued, 'a labourer was working in one of his master's fields. It was a stony field, and every time his plough hit a stone he had to stop, lay down the plough, dig out the stone and put it on the side of the field. As he was going down the field he hit something solid. When he had laid down his plough, he started to dig. However, instead of finding a stone, he found bags of treasure, the bags that the thieves had left years before. Now he knew that whatever was found in the field would belong to the person who owned the field. He stopped what he was doing, raced home to his wife and told her the news. In order to buy the field, they had to sell everything that they owned. Nevertheless, he bought the field, and then he and his wife owned the treasure. The Kingdom of God is as valuable as that treasure.'

And so it went on. More stories, more questions and answers, and still they listened. As the day wore on, the disciples were getting hungry. They noticed a tenseness in the crowd as if they too were thinking of food. One of the Twelve, Philip, came to Jesus during a pause in the teaching, and asked what they were to do about food. 'We cannot feed all these people!' he exclaimed.

'How much money do we have?' asked Jesus.

'Not enough to buy food for all these people,' replied Judas. 'There must be at least five thousand men, let alone the women and the children.'

'What are we to do?' asked Thomas.

'Have faith,' Jesus replied.

Andrew noticed a young boy, who had been sitting at the front of the crowd quite close to Jesus and had heard what was being said. Immediately, the boy came forward with the food he had been given by his mother. 'You can have my food if you wish,' he said to Jesus, and offered him a package with five flat pieces of bread and two fish. Jesus smiled at the boy and thanked him.

'Here you are, my friends,' Jesus said to the crowd.

'Remember what I said about children and their innocence. This young boy has heard us discussing the problem of food and he offers me five small loaves and two large fish to feed you all', and he held them up for all to see. There was laughter and relief. Slowly and sheepishly, people started to bring out the food that they had brought with them. They had not done so before because they did not want to have to share their food with other people. There was plenty for all, indeed so much that when everyone had finished eating there was enough to fill ten of the large baskets that merchants used for carrying goods on their backs.

'It is a miracle!' exclaimed Thomas.

'It is a miracle of love,' said Jesus.

Eventually the people started to make their way towards their homes, while the disciples and the followers of Jesus set up camp where they were. The Twelve supervised them and made sure that Jesus would not be disturbed. Just before He went off up the hillside to be on His own and pray, there were two young men waiting around to talk to Him.

'Master,' said one of them hesitatingly. 'I am a Teacher of the Law. I am ready to go with you wherever you go.'

'A Teacher needs to have a group of students whom he teaches regularly. He needs to be part of a community where he can use his scholarship. I have no home, no home base, no set community. Use your talents elsewhere.' The man turned and left, very disappointed.

The second was just as eager. 'Sir, I would like to follow You. First of all though, I need to wait until my elderly parents have died and no longer need me.'

Jesus challenged him. 'Let others look after them and see to their burial when they die. If you want to follow me, now is the time to leave all behind you and start a new life.' Jesus started to walk away from him. The young man hesitated, then turned his back on Jesus and walked down the valley.

CHAPTER 6

The Healer

AFTER two days rest, Jesus and the disciples set off again, and once more came to Capernaum. Soon after entering the town, Jesus received a message to say that a Roman Officer was looking for Him. Jesus walked towards the tax booths thinking that the soldier might be there. As He turned a corner, there was the soldier in front of him and looking very concerned. There was obvious relief when he saw Jesus, and he came towards Him as quickly as he could.

'Sir,' said the soldier, 'I am so glad to see you. I have a very dear servant who is desperately ill. Please would you heal him?'

Jesus was impressed with the man's total confidence, particularly as he was not a Jew. 'I will come with you at once,' offered Jesus.

'There is no need,' replied the officer. 'I am not worthy to have you in my home as I am part of the occupying force. Also I recognise authority when I see it. I too am under authority as well as having authority. I say to this man, "Go", and he goes. I say to another man, "Come", and he comes. I say to a third, "Do this", and he does it. So all you need to do is to command this illness to leave my servant and it will go.'

Jesus was taken aback by the soldier's faith. Turning to those following Him, He said, 'I have never come across any Jew with such faith as this!' Turning to the soldier, now kneeling at His feet, He laid His hands on him and said, 'Go in peace. Your servant is healed.' The centurion looked up, expressed his thanks, saluted Jesus, and returned to his home where, sure enough, his servant had recovered.

Later that same day, Jesus was down by the lakeside answering people's questions when there came a message from one of the leaders of the synagogue named Jairus. His daughter was seriously ill, and Jesus was needed. Immediately, Jesus and everyone listening to Him, set off. Jairus met Jesus, told Him of his daughter's illness and urged Him to make all speed.

A crowd attracts a crowd, and on this occasion more and more people joined those following Jesus out of curiosity. One woman, who had been waiting to hear about Jesus's next visit to the town, heard the noise and found the crowd and realised that Jesus must be there. She was ill. In fact she had been suffering from a regular haemorrhage for nearly twelve years. She had complete faith in Jesus but, being a woman, did not want to attract attention to herself and her condition. 'If I could just touch the hem of His garment,' she said to herself, 'I know that that would be sufficient for me to be healed.' She made up her mind that this was her opportunity for no-one in the crowd would know anything about it.

Carefully, but quite deliberately, she made her way through the crowd until she was near the front. As the crowd slowed down to turn a corner she reached out and grabbed hold of the hem of Jesus's garment. She prayed hard and immediately knew a peace of mind that she had not known for years. She had stopped in the road, and people now pushed past her.

Suddenly everyone stopped because Jesus had stopped.

'What is the matter, Lord?' asked Peter.

'Somebody touched me,' said Jesus.

'In such a crowd,' replied Peter, 'that is no great surprise,' and was about to dismiss the whole matter, but Jesus persisted.

'No, you do not understand. Someone deliberately touched me and I felt something happen,' Jesus went on.

People in the crowd were looking at one another but no one admitted anything. Jairus was anxious to get on but Jesus was adamant. The woman now felt guilty, came forward and told Jesus what she had done and why. She knelt down in front of Him and apologised.

'There is no need for this,' said Jesus. Then He laid His hands on her head and said, 'Your faith has made a healing possible. Go in peace.'

At that very moment, a servant from Jairus's home reached the crowd and told Jairus that it was too late. 'Your daughter has died.' A sadness came over the whole crowd, and Jairus looked to Jesus.

'Please, still come,' said Jairus. 'You might still be able to do something.' So Jesus and the crowd continued their journey. When they got to the house, there was such a noise. The women wailers had started their chanting, and everyone was in tears. Even the musicians had arrived ready for the funeral service. Jesus was incensed and told everyone to leave at once.

'She is not dead!' He declared. After a hesitation and a look towards Jairus, everyone did what Jesus had commanded.

Jesus, Jairus and his wife, went into the room where the little girl was lying on her bed absolutely still. Jesus held her hand, placed His hands on her head, and prayed in silence. After a time, the little girl slowly opened her eyes, saw her parents and smiled. Jairus was so relieved. After kissing his daughter and thanking Jesus, he went out to the waiting crowds and announced that his daughter was alive after all.

There was a huge cheer from the crowd, and everyone talked excitedly about what they had seen and now heard. Once again, news of Jesus's power spread throughout the whole region and beyond. Jesus stayed as a guest of Jairus.

It was now nearly a year since Jesus had been to see His home and family, so He set off once more in that direction. In one village by the lakeside, two blind men started to follow Jesus. When Jesus stopped and was invited into a nearby house, the two men also stopped but asked to see Jesus. 'Have pity on us' they shouted.

Jesus asked His host if the men could come in. When they stood in front of Him, Jesus asked them, 'Why do you believe that I can heal you?'

'Because we know that you are sent from God,' they replied.

'Then your faith will be rewarded.' Jesus stepped forward, touched their eyes with His hands, and very soon they were able to open their eyes and see. As their eyes adjusted to the light, so, naturally, they became excited. Jesus tried to restrain them. 'Now just be grateful and do not tell anyone about what has happened.' Jesus knew what the consequences would be if the men told everyone in the village. However, as soon as the men left the house, they started to tell their friends what had happened to them. Very quickly a crowd gathered outside the house, mainly of people who were ill or who had loved ones who were ill. So Jesus held a healing session.

One of the unusual healings was of a man who was dumb. His friends had brought him to Jesus. He made noises trying to talk but it was as if something were preventing him. Jesus put His hands over the man's mouth, then laid them on his head and prayed. Soon after Jesus had withdrawn His hands, the man's noises became words! He could speak! Everyone was amazed, and once again news of what had happened spread everywhere. 'We have never witnessed anything like this in the whole of Israel,' said one person.

In time, Jesus and His followers continued on their journey and eventually came to the town of Magdala. Once again, news of His arrival spread quickly. A crowd gathered and Jesus spoke to them. Suddenly the crowd parted as some Pharisees, who had heard about Jesus's reputation and His attitude to the Law, had dragged a young woman along with them and now threw her down on the ground in front of Jesus.

'This woman is a prostitute. She has been caught in the act of adultery this very morning. Now the Law of Moses quite clearly states that she must be stoned to death. What do you say?' they demanded.

Jesus sensed that this was yet another attempt to trap Him into breaking the Law, or speaking against the Law. He knelt down beside the woman. 'What is your name?' He asked.

The terrified woman whispered, 'Mary.'

'Mary,' Jesus reiterated in a voice and manner that she would never forget. Jesus was thinking of the irony of the name. His own mother was named Mary, a woman chosen to provide a normal pregnancy for Him, to bring Him into the world and to care for Him in His childhood. Now, on His way to see her once more, another Mary had come into His life. What a contrast! A prostitute, a woman who was dirty, cut and bruised, terrified. Jesus, lost in thought, drew shapes and pictures in the dust and dirt of the road.

The Pharisees were becoming impatient. 'Well?' they asked.

Jesus sat up on His heels and looked at each one in turn. 'You are quite right about the Law,' He said. 'So whichever of you has never made a mistake, pick up a stone and be the first to throw it at her.' And He bent down again and wrote in the dust. The eyes of the crowd were on the Pharisees, and they knew it. One by one the Pharisees turned and left. When they had all gone, Jesus looked up, then helped the woman to her feet. 'What has happened to your accusers?' He asked mockingly. 'Is there no-one left to condemn you?'

'Not one,' replied the woman, totally bewildered by what was happening.

'Then neither do I condemn you. But I command you, go and sin no more!' Jesus looked sternly at the woman, let go her hand, turned and walked away. That night, when Jesus, The Twelve, His disciples, and followers made camp, there, on the edge of the group, Jesus saw that same woman, Mary. She had already been made welcome by Joanna, whose husband Chuza was an officer at Herod's court, and Susanna.

Long before He reached Nazareth, people were waiting for Him. There were the usual people, the sick and those caring for them, the genuine enquirers, as well as the curious. On this occasion, officials from the Temple in Jerusalem had arrived having heard that this was where He lived. As soon as He arrived, He was swamped by all these people and dealt with them one by one. He looked worn out, and did not even make time to eat, and so there were those who came to tell His family of their concern.

Towards the end of the day, when the healing session had ended and the question and answer session had begun, those men from Jerusalem were in the crowd. Someone turned to them and asked in a loud voice, 'Well, what do you think about Jesus? Isn't He wonderful?'

The men were embarrassed at the challenge but one of them answered firmly. 'The man is a disturbed fanatic. He is using some sort of devilish power!'

Jesus heard him. 'If a country becomes involved in civil war it will tear itself apart. If a family has an almighty row they will be divided one from another and fall apart. Now if I am doing good using the power of evil, then the Devil himself must have been torn apart!' He smiled at the men. 'However if one man breaks into the home of another, ties him up and steals his wealth, he must be the stronger of the two. Imagine then that I have broken into the devil's own house, captured him, tied him up and escaped. Then I must be the stronger of the two!'

He continued to preach and teach about the Good News of God, gave the call to repentance, the offer of forgiveness, and a new beginning to people's lives. Mary, Jesus's mother, His brothers and sisters, came to find Him but could not get into the house because of the crowd. Someone shouted, 'Your mother, brothers, and sisters are here.'

'How true,' said Jesus. 'When you have come to know

and love God, then we are all indeed brothers and sisters in the family of God.'

At the end of the day, the crowds went home and Jesus and the Twelve had a meal in that same house. The representatives of the religious authority in Jerusalem were still there and when they observed some of Jesus's disciples eating without having first gone through the traditional washing of their hands, they saw their chance and challenged Jesus again.

'You allow Yourself to be called the Messiah, God's representative, yet Your own disciples do not even keep the Law on a simple matter like washing their hands,' one of their leaders announced. 'You live rough out in the countryside and one wonders if your followers wash the cups, pots, and copper bowls in the right way!' he concluded.

Jesus smiled at their pathetic attitude. 'You know, Isaiah was right when he talked about religious people who honoured God with their words but not their hearts. You are all hypocrites! You are more interested in man-made rules than in God-inspired ways of living.'

After a pause, He continued, 'You even find ways round keeping the Law of Moses. The Law says "Honour your father and mother." Now surely that implies helping them when they are in need. So imagine that your mother and father need financial help. What do you do? You claim that you cannot give them any money because all your money is bound by the rule of Corban, in other words you have dedicated it solely to the work of God! Can't you see that it may well be the will of God to help your parents with that money? You manipulate the Law to serve your own purposes and that is hypocrisy!'

He went on, 'Let us look at this nonsense about what is clean and what is unclean. You have rules about food. Nothing that goes into a man can make him unclean. It is what comes out of a man that makes him unclean, and I do not mean human waste. It is his heart that matters, not his stomach. If he is immoral, if he is involved in criminal activities, if he is deceitful, hypocritical and irreligious, then he is unclean!'

The men could stand no more of Jesus's challenges, and they went away.

That night, Jesus returned home while the Twelve joined His disciples and followers who had already made camp outside the town. Jesus knew that this visit was likely to be the last one that He would make. Soon He would have to make His way to Jerusalem, and there would be no way back from that encounter.

CHAPTER 7

New Territory

THE Twelve were now in for a shock. After the morning meal, Jesus took the Twelve apart and told them that they were now going to be involved in the task of ministry. 'The time will come when the authorities will end my ministry one way or another, and you must then become my mouth, hands and feet. Now is the time to start our practical training while I am still with you.'

'But Lord,' butted in Thomas, 'we cannot do what you do.'

'Oh yes you can,' replied Jesus quickly. 'If you have sufficient faith in God, then you can do all that I can do, in fact you could do even greater things.' The Twelve were stunned by His words, and each looked at the other with considerable trepidation. 'I want you to go in faith, so do not take any money in your pockets, any food or extra clothing, but do not give the impression that you are a beggar. Take a stick for protection and wear sandals to protect your feet. Go out two by two. When you come to a town or village, accept its hospitality and preach the Good News of God. If you are not accepted, and the people will not listen to you, then make a show of shaking the dust off your feet as you leave as a sign that they have missed a great opportunity.'

When it was clear that Jesus was perfectly serious, Peter started to organise them into twos. Peter went with Andrew; James and John were to go together, as were Philip and Nathaniel. Judas and Simon teamed up together, Matthew went with his brother James, and that left Thaddaeus and Thomas.

Jesus held a question and answer session with them. They prayed together, and finally Jesus gave them His blessing and sent them off in different directions.

A week later, they began to return. All of them had stories to tell, and many of those stories were of success. People had listened to the Good News, had repented of their sins, and had committed themselves to starting a new life. Some reported that people had been healed, particularly those who were disturbed in their minds. 'It was as if evil spirits had been removed from them and they now knew peace of mind!' one of the Twelve reported. There was great rejoicing in the camp, and the Twelve now took on a new status amongst the disciples and followers of Jesus. They now had a new role to play.

The town of Tiberias had once upon a time given its name to the lake. Many people knew the Lake as Gennesaret, others as that of Galilee. Jesus was now known as 'the Galilean' even though His home town was Nazareth. So much of His ministry had been around the towns and villages of Lake Galilee that they were now proud to own Him as their own special prophet. So Jesus the Galilean came into the town of Tiberias.

The town not only had a Roman name but an air of importance. Because Jews were forbidden to enter it, Jesus held teaching sessions and times for healing on the outskirts.

People knew of the success of His ministry so far. One person once asked Him, 'Will this Kingdom of God that you keep talking about, like the Roman Empire, continue to grow and expand?'

Jesus replied, 'The Kingdom of God is like a mustard seed. Now this seed is one of the smallest seeds. However, when you plant it and tend it, it grows into a small tree big enough even for birds to build their nests in it.'

Another man, one of the judges in the town, asked Jesus, 'Who will decide who can be a citizen in this Kingdom?'

Jesus answered, 'the same rules you use for making your judgements will be made by God. He knows everything there is to know about everyone. He knows who is telling the truth and who is not. He will make sure that everyone who is trying to hide something will be exposed. He will be just and impartial so that those who have succeeded honestly will be rewarded, and those who have failed through dishonesty, even what they have will be taken away from them.'

That evening, Jesus said to the Twelve, 'let us go across to the other side of the lake.' They hired a boat and set off in order to cross the lake. Here the distance is only about five miles but the weather suddenly changed and a fierce storm struck the lake. Jesus had lain down in the back of the boat and had gone to sleep. Even though Peter and some of the others were experienced fishermen, the storm was so bad that the boat began to ship water and the men were afraid the boat was going to sink. The sky also became very dark.

Thomas went to Jesus and shook Him in order to wake Him. 'Master, wake up! We're sinking! Don't you care?'

'Calm down,' said Jesus to Thomas. 'Nothing is going to happen to us.' Then He stood up and went to the prow of the ship. He gazed out across the lake. 'Why are you so frightened? Where is your faith?' He asked the others. Then He turned facing the wind and said, 'It will soon be still!' Sure enough, in a matter of minutes the wind died down, the lake became calm and they continued on their way.

'Amazing!' exclaimed Andrew who had been genuinely afraid. 'Even the wind and the water obey Him.'

By the time they had crossed the lake, it was late but Jesus had already sent some of His followers on ahead in order to make camp for the night. When they found them they were glad of the company for most of the Twelve had been badly shaken.

In the morning, they looked round at their surroundings. There were some limestone cliffs with quite a number of caves in them. Then they realised that this was used as a cemetery by people from a nearby town. Suddenly there was a shriek from one of the women for she noticed a man coming out of one of the tombs. His wrists and feet were raw and bleeding, and it was obvious that at some time he had been chained up but had escaped. They learnt later that he was well known in the area and usually wandered in and out of the tombs, shouting and screaming, falling down and cutting himself on the stones. He was a very disturbed individual.

Jesus stepped forward immediately and moved in the direction of the man. Seeing Jesus, the man ran towards Him and then fell at His feet.

'What do you want with me?' the man challenged Jesus. 'Don't punish me anymore, I beg of you! I know who You are. You are the man from God. Don't hurt me!' he shouted.

Jesus asked him, 'What is your name?'

'My name is Legion,' he replied, 'for there are so many of us.'

Jesus talked quietly with him, laid His hands on his head and prayed with him. Then Jesus put His hands on either side of the man's head and prayed loudly, as if we were shouting at somebody. 'Be at peace!' He said.

Suddenly the man let out a piercing yell and it echoed all around the area. The disciples and followers were terrified. Suddenly there was a rumbling from on top of the cliffs. The man's yell must have frightened a herd of pigs that were grazing on the top. They all panicked, and, squealing at the same time, ran at full speed in the direction of the cliffs. Before anyone could do anything about it, the whole herd went straight over the cliff and fell to the rocks below. Nobody moved, shocked by what had happened and frightened by the noise.

While they were standing looking, some men appeared on top of the cliff. They were obviously in charge of the herd of pigs and were looking to see what had happened and who was responsible. Seeing Jesus, and the demented man standing calmly by Him, they automatically assumed that Jesus was responsible. They ran back to tell the pig farmers for whom they worked, what had happened, making sure that they would not be blamed. The pigs were valuable because they could be sold to Greek people in the towns of Decapolis, for the pigs were honoured by them and would be used for sacrifices.

When the farmers arrived on the scene and saw the sick man now clothed and in his right mind, they too assumed that Jesus was responsible. They demanded compensation for their herds and ordered Jesus to leave their territory.

In order to restore peace, Jesus got into the boat, gave instructions to His followers to break camp and move on, and ordered Peter to set sail.

The man who had been healed, came to the boat. 'May I go with You?' he asked.

Jesus replied, 'No. You are in no danger. Go to the authorities in your home town, show them that you are now well again and make sure that they pronounce you officially 'clean'. Then you can go back to your family and start your life all over again.' Reluctantly he did what Jesus said, but what a story he was able to tell to everyone he met!

Meanwhile, Jesus and the Twelve set off in the boat and landed at the lakeside town of Hippos. It was nearly two years since Jesus had made His way from Aenon where He had been baptised by John, through the Ten Towns, to begin His ministry in Galilee. People had no idea who He was then but now it was different. There were those who had travelled across the lake to Capernaum and heard Him preach and seen Him heal. Now, when Jesus came to them, crowds of people came to listen and to be healed. Once again Jesus found a responsive people.

People here told Him of their difficulties and He responded by saying to them, 'Come to me, all of you who feel that you are carrying great burdens. I will help you to find rest, that is peace of mind. Now you carry a yoke round your neck for transporting goods from one place to another. My yoke, however, is easy and my burden is light because it is from God. Help carry the Good News of God to all people.'

One evening, when talking with the Twelve, He said, 'There is a large harvest to be gathered in but there are so few workers. I must pray to the vineyard owner to provide more workers.' He left them to be on His own to pray.

After the ministry in the Ten Towns, Jesus and His disciples went north, past Lake Huleh and across to the Western coast and the towns of Tyre and Sidon in the region of Syro-Phoenicia. Many people had already seen and heard Jesus in Capernaum and the neighbouring areas, and His welcome was just as enthusiastic as elsewhere, though here there was considerable tension between the Jews and foreigners living in the towns.

On one occasion, Jesus and The Twelve were guests in someone's house and having a meal when a woman shouted to Jesus for help. It turned out that she was a foreigner but was living in the town. 'Jesus, have mercy on my daughter,' she shouted. 'She is in a terrible condition and no-one can help her.'

The disciples were embarrassed that such a woman should make a fuss while they were in someone's house and having a meal. Nathaniel begged Jesus, 'send her away. She has been following us and making a nuisance of herself.'

The woman then forced her way in and fell at Jesus's feet. 'Please help me, sir,' she said desperately.

Jesus was conscious that His Jewish host and his guests were watching Him carefully. 'Surely it is right that the Children of Israel should be fed first,' Jesus said to her. 'It is not right to take their food and throw it out for the dogs to eat.'

'No sir,' replied the woman, 'but even the dogs eat the leftovers from the master's table.'

Jesus smiled, laid His hands on her head and said, 'Go in peace, your daughter has been healed.'

And so the ministry continued, following the same pattern

with once again the Twelve being sent out as part of their training. Jesus carefully warned them, however, so that they would be in no doubt as to the difficulties.

In Sidon, a man who was deaf and had a speech impediment, was brought to Him for healing. Those who had brought him begged Jesus to help him. Jesus took the man away from the crowds, but with two of the Twelve, so that they could be on their own. As usual He talked with the man, prayed with Him and then prepared for the man's healing. First He put His fingers into the man's ears. Then He put His fingers on the man's tongue. Looking straight at the man's head, Jesus said 'Be opened.' After a few moments, the man began to talk without any impediment, and when the two disciples started to talk he heard what they were saying. He was so excited that he ran back to the crowd and they were all amazed listening to his shouts of joy. Jesus tried to get the people in the crowd not to be too excited or spread the news of what had happened, but they took no notice.

'Isn't He wonderful,' they said, 'He can even make the deaf hear and the dumb speak!' As a result, crowds of people came for healing, and Jesus helped each one.

In time, after many months, Jesus and the Twelve returned to Capernaum. However, they were conscious that there was a different atmosphere and attitude. The sick were still glad to see Jesus, but the enthusiastic crowds were gone. He realised that part of this was due to the fact that He had been away so long. The Pharisees had taken advantage of this absence to re-establish their hold on the people, and the people themselves had returned to their old ways.

Some Pharisees came to Jesus and started an argument with Him. Once again they were not interested in Him and what He had to say, but wanted merely to trap Him into breaking the Law so that they could discredit Him in front of the ordinary people.

'Perform a miracle for us now so that we can believe you!' they demanded.

Jesus replied, 'Why do you now demand a miracle? No, that is not my way. I will not go back on my decision. Believe my words, or at least what you have seen in the changed lives of people and those who have been healed.' He looked at them defiantly. 'When the sun is setting, you say, "We are going to have fine weather because the sky is red." And early in the morning, you say, "We are going to have rain because the sky is red." You can predict the weather by looking at the sky, but you cannot predict what is going to happen to people because you cannot see what is happening around you. People are being offered a new beginning to their lives but all you are interested in is seeing a miracle. If I swim out into the lake, get swallowed by a great fish like Jonah and thrown out on the shore at Bethsaida, will that do? No! No such miraculous proof will be given!'

When Jesus realised the extent of the problem, having talked with many of His friends in the town, He ordered His whole company to move to Bethsaida. The followers went round the northern shore of the lake while Jesus and the Twelve crossed over in boats. When they got to the other side, they had a long time to wait for the followers to reach them and set up camp. The disciples realised that they had not brought anything to eat.

'Lord, in the midst of all that heated discussion on the other side, we have forgotten to buy bread.'

Jesus said, still thinking of what had happened at Capernaum, 'why bother about bread? How little real concern you have for the faith. Don't you understand yet? Beware of the yeast of the Pharisees. Their influence permeates the whole of society and works against all that I am trying to do.'

Next day in Bethsaida, some people brought a blind man to Jesus and begged Jesus to heal him. Jesus once again led the man out of the town so that they could be away from the crowd. He talked with the man, prayed with him, and prepared a mixture of spit and dust. He rubbed the mud onto the man's eyes, placed His hands on the man's head and commanded, 'Be healed.' After a few moments, the man opened his eyes.

'What can you see?' asked Jesus.

'I see men, standing like trees, but walking about!' he replied.

'Good,' said Jesus. 'The healing is beginning.' Indeed the man could soon see clearly. However, Jesus asked him not to go back into the town just yet.

Jesus and the Twelve went on to Chorazin but, like Bethsaida and Capernaum, the attitude had changed and many people had returned to their old ways of life. Jesus was saddened. As He looked round He said, 'You do not realise the mistake that you are making. In Tyre and Sidon, there was genuine repentance and people's lives have been changed. When they come face to face with God on their day of Judgement, they will receive His loving forgiveness and He will show them His mercy. But you? Here in Chorazin, at Bethsaida, and even in Capernaum, you were given a wonderful opportunity and seemed to grasp it. But now I find that you have thrown it all aside. It will be tragic for you on your day of Judgement.'

He went on. 'You see your fishermen. They come back with their boats laden with all sorts of fish. They bring their catch to shore and divide it up. The good ones they throw into buckets for selling while the worthless are thrown away. Beware! You too may be thrown away as worthless if you reject the Good News of God.'

And so the Galilean ministry came to an end in the midst of disappointment. Jesus and His disciples set off north towards Ceasarea Philippi beyond the northern lake and in sight of Mount Hermon.

On the way He warned the Twelve, 'You can see for yourselves that I am sending you out like sheep amongst wolves. You must be as cautious as snakes but as gentle as doves. Be careful, for just as I shall one day be arrested and brought before the courts, so, in time, they will turn against you. When they do, do not worry about what to say or how to say it for God will inspire you and give you the words that you will need.'

Later He warned them, 'We are offering people Good News from God but there are those who will perceive it as a challenge to their authority and their tradition. People are reluctant to change. Husband and wife will disagree, parents and children will be divided, even brother will turn against brother. Do not lose courage or hope. If they persecute you in one town, then go on to another. Remember to follow my example, for a slave is not greater than his master, nor a student greater than his teacher. Hold on to the faith. They may kill the body but they cannot destroy the soul. God knows you and loves you for everyone matters to Him.'

And so with much teaching and further warnings, Jesus and His followers arrived and set up camp north of the town of Caesarea Philippi.

At an evening session with the Twelve, Jesus asked them, 'Who do people think I am?'

'Some say John the Baptist,' said John.

'Others say Elijah,' added James.

'I have heard people say Jeremiah or one of the prophets,' said Matthew.

Then Jesus looked at them in turn. 'And what do you think?'

Peter jumped to his feet. 'You are the Messiah, the Son of the living God!' he exclaimed.

Jesus smiled at his typical Galilean fervour. 'Good for you, Peter. You have been truly inspired by God, and you will be the leader of the Twelve when I have left you.' Then, with Mount Hermon as a back drop He declared, 'You are like a rock, strong, firm and solid, and the new community of faith will be built on you.'

During the time that they all spent together, the disciples gained the impression that this was the end of the beginning and the beginning of the end. On one occasion, for example, Jesus talked about His future.

'Now the challenge must be taken to Jerusalem itself. There the authorities, Jewish and Roman alike, will feel strong enough to stand up to the people and their response. There will be much suffering. I shall be arrested, brought before the courts, condemned and executed. But all this will prove who I am and answer the questions of why I am here. Then you will see for yourselves the almighty power of God for He cannot be defeated.' He ended on a note of triumph.

Peter, however, was only listening to the prediction about Jesus's death. 'Never, Lord!' he exclaimed. 'I will never let anything happen to you.'

'Oh Peter,' Jesus sighed, 'you have so much to learn. You sound courageous now but when you are really up against it, you will lose your courage, run away and deny me!'

'Never, Lord, never,' protested Peter fervently.

Jesus went on, 'If anyone wants to follow me, he will have to take up a cross like me. Whoever wants to find the best life that there is will need to lose it by giving His life to me and for me. The Messiah is about to face His greatest challenge. But don't be afraid! You will all see the glory of God!'

From that moment on, He set His face towards Jerusalem. This first part of His ministry was completed.

PART TWO

FROM

CAESAREA PHILIPPI

TO

BETHANY

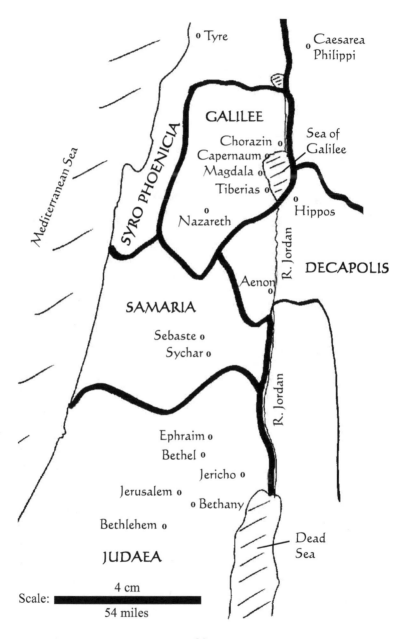

Scale:

4 cm

54 miles

Tyre, Caesarea Philippi, GALILEE, Chorazin, Sea of Galilee, SYRO PHOENICIA, Mediterranean Sea, Capernaum, Magdala, Tiberias, Nazareth, Hippos, R. Jordan, DECAPOLIS, Aenon, SAMARIA, Sebaste, Sychar, R. Jordan, Ephraim, Bethel, Jericho, Jerusalem, Bethany, Bethlehem, JUDAEA, Dead Sea

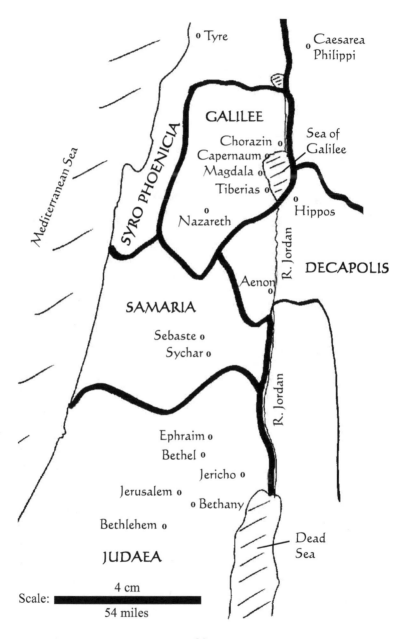

Scale: 4 cm / 54 miles

CHAPTER 1

Galilee

THERE was a great sense of purpose as the followers of Jesus struck camp and began the long journey to Jerusalem. As most of them came from the towns and villages round the Lake of Galilee, there would be an opportunity for them to go home before continuing on their way south. Chorazin was their first main stop.

On the Sabbath day, Jesus went to the synagogue as usual. When He entered, there began a wave of conversation for the congregation and the synagogue leaders remembered His last visit. Jesus noticed a woman trying to go up the steps to the women's gallery. She was bent over almost double through illness. Jesus found out later that she had been like that for eighteen years. He called to her. She stopped to locate the voice. Jesus moved towards her. He was so sympathetic to her plight that He placed His hands on her there and then and prayed for her and with her. After a few minutes He helped her to straighten up. The women in the gallery were so thrilled that they started to sing praise songs.

The leader of the synagogue was furious. He turned on Jesus and blamed Him for disturbing the congregation and deliberately breaking the Sabbath laws. 'There are six days in which to do this sort of thing, but not on the Sabbath.'

Jesus shook His head in disappointment. 'You hypocrites!' He exclaimed. 'You would not hesitate, on the Sabbath, to untie your ox or your donkey from its stall and lead it to water to drink. That is work, according to the Law. Yet you would tie my hands so that this woman would not be healed!' His answer made some of the congregation feel ashamed while others joined the women in singing praises to God.

At Chorazin, Jesus encouraged those who could to go and celebrate the Passover with their families while the rest stayed in the homes of other followers and well-wishers. 'Next year we shall celebrate it in Jerusalem,' He said, with echoes of the Passover service itself. Jesus went with James and John to visit Zebedee in the family home at Bethsaida, and shared the family Passover with them. While Jesus was there, Zebedee's wife came to Jesus and asked, 'Promise me that when you come into your kingdom, my two sons will be able to sit on the right and left hand sides of your throne.'

Jesus replied, 'You do not know what you are asking. I do not have the right to make those decisions. My Father in heaven will make those decisions.'

On the way to Capernaum, Jesus was conscious that the Twelve were arguing amongst themselves. Something about what had been said at Bethsaida must have been mentioned. So when they reached Capernaum and had settled down for a meal, He asked them, 'What were you arguing about on the road?'

They did not answer Jesus because they were ashamed. They had been arguing about who was the most important member of the Twelve. There were some children playing nearby. Jesus said to one of the children, 'Come and stand here in front of everyone.' The child did so. He was a boy and he stood up straight as if proud to have been chosen. Jesus, who knew what they had been discussing, said, 'Whoever wants to be first must be ready to be placed last. Those who want to lead must be prepared to serve. Those who want to give orders must be ready, like this little boy, to obey orders. Everybody matters to God equally. Whoever welcomes a child in my name welcomes me and whoever welcomes me welcomes the one who sent me.'

He let the little boy go and return to his friends. 'It is our responsibility to set a good example at all times, particularly in front of the children. If anyone should cause one of these little ones to stumble and lose faith in me, it would be better for that person to have a large millstone tied round his neck and be thrown into the lake.'

Jesus went on to challenge them about the seriousness of their conduct.

'If something you do with your hand causes you to lose faith, cut it off! It is better to enter eternal life with only one hand than to miss out entirely. Similarly, if your foot causes you to stumble in spiritual terms, cut it off! It is better to enter heaven with one foot than to go to hell with both feet. So also with your eyes. If one of your eyes causes you to falter and fall, pluck it out. It is better to enter heaven partially blind than to jump headlong into the fiery pit with both eyes.' The disciples were amazed at what Jesus was saying, though realising that in a way He was teasing them while teaching them as well.

'Also, if your friend or brother leads you astray or sins against you, go and show him his fault. But do it privately, just between yourselves. If he listens to you, then your relationship is back to normal. If he fails to listen, try again and take someone else with you to corroborate what you are saying and thus try and make peace between you.'

Peter asked, 'But how often should one forgive? Seven

times?'

'No, not seven times,' Jesus replied, 'but seventy times seven.' Peter shook his head. 'The Kingdom of Heaven is like this,' Jesus continued. 'Once there was a King who called for his treasurer to call in all the debts that were outstanding. One of the accounts was for a great deal of money. The man responsible did not have enough money to pay the debt. The king ordered him to be sold as a slave, with his wife and children and all that he had, in order to pay off the debt. The man fell on his knees in front of the king. "Be patient with me, sir," he begged, "and I will pay you everything I owe you." The king felt sorry for him, forgave him the debt, and let him go.'

'This same man went out and met one of those men who owed him just a small amount. He grabbed him by the throat, nearly choking him to death, demanding his money back. When he released him, the man fell to his knees and begged for patience.

'Give me a little time,' he said, 'and I will pay you back.' But the first man refused and had this last man thrown into prison until the debt was paid.'

'Word got back to the king that the servant that he had forgiven had maltreated someone who owed him money. The king called him back. 'You worthless subject,' he said. 'I forgave you the whole amount you owed me because of your plea. In turn you should have had mercy on your debtor.' The king had him punished by throwing him into prison.

'Now,' said Jesus, 'learn to forgive others just as God your heavenly Father forgives you.'

Later that day, John reported to Jesus that he had seen a man healing people of evil spirits. 'He claims to heal in your name but he does not belong to our group!' he exclaimed.

'Do not try to stop him,' Jesus replied. 'Anyone who performs a miracle in my name will bring honour to me and the One who sent me. Whoever is not against us is for us. He will receive his reward.'

When they came to Magdala, Jesus thought that Mary might want to go into the town. Some of the followers went to share the evening meal with friends and family, but Mary stayed in the camp. She served Jesus His meal and sat close to Him.

'Is there no-one you would like to visit?' asked Jesus.

'No,' Mary said quickly, and then added, 'thank you. I have had a new life since then and I do not want to be reminded of my past.' Jesus understood and said nothing more. Later on Mary asked Jesus, 'You said that the authorities will arrest you and kill you. Yet you have the power to do anything. Why would you let that happen?'

Jesus replied, 'It is one of the inevitable consequences of my life. The offer of new life is for everyone. However, for the authorities this is seen as a challenge to their authority and control, another false Messiah to be removed from society like a leper.' Mary's eyes began to fill with tears. 'But do not lose faith,' Jesus continued reassuringly. 'Though I may have to die, then God's power will be truly shown for I will return and you will be one of the first to see me, I promise.' Gently He lifted her chin with His finger and smiled. For a moment she held on to His finger.

Later Jesus was invited to a meal at the home of a rich Pharisee. Such meals were often eaten outside in the courtyard so that other people could view the meal. In this case there was going to be a guest speaker so people would gather to watch the guests arriving, watch the meal and then listen to the speaker. The guests were also very conscious of the crowd of people around them, and the Pharisees in particular were keen to make a good impression.

As this was a Sabbath Day, the meal was a cold meal for there could be no work, no cooking of food. Just after the meal had started, a man came out of the crowd and came towards Jesus. He had swollen arms and legs. It was obvious to Jesus, as well as to everyone else, that this was a deliberate ploy by the Pharisees, which meant that in fact the whole meal and invitation were an elaborate means to trap Him into making a mistake.

Jesus, well aware of what was happening, asked His host and the other Pharisees gathered there, 'Does our Law allow healing on the Sabbath?' Everyone, of course, knew the answer.

However, no-one said a word. The tension was considerable. Jesus got up from the table, took hold of the man, prayed with him and then asked a healing blessing on him. Very quickly the swellings eased and the man was obviously being healed. The heads of the Pharisees were shaking in disgust while inside they were smiling. The plot had been successful.

While they were enjoying their triumph, Jesus, still on His feet, asked them a question. 'Suppose it is a Sabbath Day. Your own son falls into a deep ravine. Are you going to leave him there or pull him out?' There was no reply but His point had got home. Jesus returned to His place and the meal continued.

When it was time for Him to speak, He quickly turned from defence into attack in His dealings with the Pharisaic guests. 'When someone invites you to a feast, do not try and sit in the seats for the special guests, trying to impress other people with your self-importance, as some of you did this evening. If someone more important than you comes, then you will have to suffer the embarrassment of being moved further from your host. On the other hand, if you sit in the seats away from your host, when he comes in he will see where you are and then invite you to come and sit near him. Think of the honour this will be. Beware then of your arrogance and your vanity, for, in the Kingdom of God, the self-important will be humbled and the meek will be honoured.'

Then Jesus turned to His host who quite obviously had been part of the plot. 'When you invite people to a meal,' He said, 'don't invite your family or your friends. They will in turn invite you into their homes for a meal and then you will be repaid for your hospitality. No, go to the people who are in greatest need, those who cannot repay with a meal and have no home to which to invite you. Go to the poor, the crippled, the lame and the blind. God will repay you in heaven for your generosity.'

One of the other guests remarked aloud, 'How happy then are those who will sit down at the table for the Heavenly banquet.'

Jesus looked at him and then said to everyone, 'Once upon a time there was a rich man who decided to host a great feast.

'He drew up his guest list of important people and then sent out the invitations. Later, when all the arrangements had been made, he sent further messages to tell his guests that the meal was now ready and that he looked forward to seeing them. However, one by one, they all made their apologies. One man said, "I have just bought a field to add to my property and I want to go and see what it is like. Sorry that I shall not be able to come to the feast." Another said, "I have just bought a new team of oxen and I want to go and try them out. Sorry I shall not be able to come to the feast." A third one said, "I have just got married and I am on my honeymoon. Sorry!" Everyone had an excuse. No-one was coming to the feast.

'The host was furious. Then he said to his servants, "Go out into the roads and the alleyways of the town. Go out into the countryside. When you meet someone, whoever they are, the poor, the crippled, the lame and the blind, urge them to come in and share this meal. I shall never invite those special guests again.'

Jesus paused. 'The Lord God has invited you to follow Him but you have been too busy with your own affairs and you have ignored His invitations. However, the people for whom you have little concern, the casualties of our society, and those whom you despise, like the prostitutes and the collaborators, these are the people who will accept God's invitation and they will share in the Messianic banquet instead of you!'

When it was time to move on, the disciples, at this stage in the journey, were interested to see which route Jesus would take. Most pilgrims to Jerusalem went through Decapolis on the other side of the Jordan rather than go through Samaria. The Jews hated the Samaritans and no-one wanted to court disaster by travelling through their country.

Jesus, however, turned quite deliberately onto the main road south with every intention of travelling through Samaria.

CHAPTER 2

Samaria

WHILE travelling through a particularly barren stretch of the Samaritan countryside, on the way to Sebaste, Jesus and the Twelve noticed a group of ten bedraggled looking men, standing near the roadside and saying something as if in warning. As the disciples got nearer to them, Nathaniel touched Jesus's arm and said, 'Lord, be careful, they are lepers.' Eventually they could make out the words.

'Unclean, unclean, unclean,' they were shouting, which added to their pathetic appearance. The disciples hesitated, but Jesus, moved with compassion, deliberately went towards them. 'Have pity on us, sir,' one of them said. 'Give us some money, sir, to buy food in the nearby village,' said another one of them encouraged by Jesus's attitude. Several of the others quickly joined in the appeal.

'I can do better than that,' Jesus said. He went to each one in turn, placed His hands on their heads, asking a healing blessing upon them and prayed with them. Then He took some money out of the purse that Judas was carrying and gave it to them. 'Now, clean yourselves up, go into the village, and then show yourselves to the priests in the synagogue. By the time you have reached them, you will be healed. The priests can then declare you clean once more.'

The lepers were astounded. No-one had shown them such compassion. They looked at their hands and faces and believed that something was already happening. Jesus moved on, and the disciples, giving the lepers a wide berth, followed Him. They noticed that two of them were helping a third who seemed very weak and out of his mind.

Jesus and the followers set up camp outside the village while Judas and Matthew went into the village to buy food and something for them to drink. Later, while they were eating their evening meal, one of the former lepers came out of the village to see Jesus.

Hesitatingly, he approached the camp.

'Come on in,' said Jesus.

'I have come to say thank you, sir, for your kindness. It all happened just as you said,' and he showed Jesus his arms and legs.

'Good,' replied Jesus. 'But weren't there ten of you?'

'Yes sir,' replied the man, embarrassed that he was the only one.

'Do not worry,' Jesus said. 'Your faith in me has made you well.' The man left and returned to the village. 'Did you notice,' Jesus said to the followers, 'It was the Samaritan, the dreaded foreigner, who came to say "Thank You"?'

'It would have been better if he had brought us some food as a way of saying "thank you",' Judas complained. 'We are running short of money again.'

'What are you doing with it all?' teased Alphaeus.

'If you can do better,' challenged Judas, failing to appreciate that he was being teased, 'you take over being the treasurer!'

There was an uneasy atmosphere between them for some time afterwards.

After the meal was over, Jesus told them this story. 'There was once a very rich man, an absentee landlord, who had an old servant who was in charge of all the property. The manager was a generous man, liked to make friends and tried to help everyone who came to him for help. The rich man was warned by others on his estate that his manager was cheating him. The manager was called in to see the owner. 'What is this I hear about you?' asked the owner. 'I want you to furnish me with your complete account books. If these complaints are substantiated, then I shall dismiss you from your position.'

The manager was very concerned. 'What on earth shall I do?' he asked himself. 'It sounds as if he is going to dismiss me,' he thought, 'and where then shall I get work? I am not strong enough to dig ditches; I am too old to do most jobs, and I am too proud to beg.' After a time worrying about losing his friends as well as his job, he had a good idea. So he sent word to all those to whom he had lent his master's money. He asked the first one, 'How much do you owe?' 'I bought one hundred barrels of olive oil with it. Whatever that costs now!' 'All right,' said the manager, 'here is a bill for half of that. Please pay it straight away.' To another he asked the same question. 'To the value of a thousand sacks of wheat,' the man replied. 'Here is a bill to the value of eight hundred sacks. Please pay it straight away.' And he did the same for everyone else. 'At least,' he said to himself, 'I shall keep my friends.'

When the manager appeared before his master, he showed him the accounts and the way in which he had tried to recover much of what had been lent out. The owner shook his head in dismay at the accounts, but commended the manager for his shrewd attempt to hold onto his friends.'

Jesus continued, 'Worldly wealth may have some material blessings but real friendships will serve you well in this life and in the life to come. If you learn what is of most value in the ordinary and everyday affairs of life, then you are more likely to learn what is of ultimate value in life itself. However, no man can put material blessings and spiritual blessings first in his life. He has to decide, one or the other. He has to decide what matters most. You cannot serve God and the god of materialism at the same time.'

Jesus drove this message home with another story. 'There was once a rich man who had land which bore good crops. He began to realise that he did not have enough barns in which to store all his grain. "What shall I do?" he asked himself. Answering his own question, he said, "I will pull down my barns and build bigger ones. There I will store all my grain and everything else that I have accrued. Then I will say to myself, what a lucky man I am. I now have all that I need for years to come. I will eat, drink and take life easy. I will enjoy myself."

'But God said to him, "You fool! This very night you will have to give up your life. Now who will get the benefit of all your wealth?"

'That is the danger,' Jesus continued, 'for those who value worldly wealth above spiritual wealth. They pile up riches on earth but do not take time to make spiritual wealth.'

The following morning they broke camp and continued on their journey to Sebaste. Jesus had, as usual, taken time before breakfast to pray and had found a quiet place away from the camp. As He returned, He saw two men, one supporting the other, walking along the road. One indicated to Jesus that he wanted to speak with Him. Jesus came to them and realised that they were two of the lepers whom He had healed.

'We have come to say "thank you", said the stronger of the two. My name is Simon and my friend and neighbour is Lazarus. We are,' he paused, 'were, merchants. We were on a ship from Rome to Caesarea when men were taken sick. Before anyone realised the gravity of the situation, warning was given that leprosy had been diagnosed. Ten of us developed the disease and were isolated in part of the ship. When we got to Caesarea, the boat was not allowed into the port. We were taken off first and rowed in a dingy to part of the coast well away from the town. The other passengers and crew were disembarked and then the boat, including the cargo, was burnt at sea. We sat on the shore and watched it burn. We have lost everything. We started off from the beach, cutting across country, in the hope of getting home to Bethany, near Jerusalem, using the road as a guide, though keeping off it because of travellers like yourselves. It has been a terrible ordeal but we are in your debt. If you ever go to Jerusalem, please call at our home in the nearby village of Bethany and we will entertain you with great joy.'

They talked for a while. Then Jesus arranged for them to be given some more money from the bag that Judas was carrying in order to buy a donkey in the village. 'God bless you sir,' said Simon.

'Peace be with you,' replied Jesus, and they all moved on.

Soon afterwards, some men from Sebaste came out to see Jesus. 'You are forbidden to enter our town,' said their leader. It was obvious that they had already been warned about the strangers and the lepers. The people were terrified they would catch the dreaded disease. Jesus acknowledged their order and made no attempt to countermand it.

When they had gone, James and John, embarrassed and annoyed by these Samaritans, came to Jesus and asked, 'Will You call down fire from heaven to destroy the village for this rebuke?'

'No,' said Jesus, 'their fears are understandable,' and lovingly, but firmly, told them off for their nationalist pride and resentment.

Later that day they came to Jacob's Well, a famous landmark at the foot of Mount Gerizim and a place to which many pilgrims came. Jesus decided to make camp near the well, but He sent His followers into the nearby town, Sychar, to shop and look around. John tried to persuade Jesus to go with them, and then Philip offered to stay with Jesus. However, He refused all offers and they left Him on His own, presuming that He wanted the time to pray. It was about noon, and He sat down on the edge of the well and noticed that there was no bucket. A woman arrived carrying a pitcher and a wooden bucket, tired from her journey from the town. She was a Samaritan, and, recognising that the man at the well was a Jew, she knew full well that He would not speak to her and that she must not speak to Him.

However when she arrived at the well, Jesus greeted her. 'Peace be with you,' He said.

The woman was taken aback, but courteously responded to His greeting. She then attached her bucket to the well rope and lowered the bucket into the well. It was some time before there was a splash which indicated that the bucket had reached the water level. Quickly she turned the handle again and the bucket was brought to the top of the well. She had a drink of water herself from a small cup that she had tied to the neck of the pitcher and then poured the rest of the water from the bucket into the pitcher. She was about to repeat the action when Jesus asked her, 'Please may I have a drink of water?'

Now, no self-respecting Jew would drink from anything that had been used by a Samaritan, and certainly not with them. The woman therefore was naturally shocked, and said, 'Sir, I am a Samaritan and you are a Jew. You will not now use this bucket and cup, and so you have no cup from which to drink.'

Jesus looked at her. 'If you knew who I am, it would be you asking me for water, water that would last for ever.'

'But sir,' she replied, 'you have not got a bucket so how can you get this special water? It was our ancestor Jacob who gave us this well and it has lasted through all the generations since. Now, are you greater than Jacob?'

Jesus responded, 'Whoever drinks from this water will soon be thirsty again. But whoever drinks from the water of life will never need another drink of water.'

'Oh sir,' she said, 'give me some of that water, then I shall no longer be thirsty but also I shall not need to keep trekking out to this well everyday!' She lowered the bucket once more. This time she offered Him the opportunity of dipping His hands in the water, making a cup shape with them and drinking from the water. It was very refreshing. They sat looking at the view of the nearby mountains. 'It is a lovely view,' she said. 'I find it easy to worship God out here in the peace and quiet, as well as in our own Temple.' After a pause, she asked Jesus, 'Our ancestors have worshipped here for so long. Why do you Jews say that Jerusalem is the only place where someone can worship God?'

Jesus replied, 'Believe me, soon there will be no city of Jerusalem where anyone can worship. It is not the buildings or the mountains where worship is to be conducted but in the hearts of men and women. God's Spirit will bless you for God is Spirit and all those who truly worship Him worship Him in spirit as well.'

The woman did not understand what Jesus was saying, but was impressed by the way He spoke. She stood up as if to go. 'I know that one day the Messiah will come and then we shall understand everything.'

'I am He,' replied Jesus, 'The one with whom you are talking.' She stood there amazed, but before she could say anything she heard the noise of the Followers returning from the town. Aware of the customs of Jews and Samaritans, she quickly lifted the pitcher onto her head, with the cup inside and the bucket attached, and returned to her home.

The disciples realised that Jesus had been talking to her and were amazed. 'Why on earth were you talking to that woman?' asked Matthew. 'What did she want?' he continued, obviously assuming that Jesus would never have initiated the conversation. They set up camp near the well. When the meal was ready, they called Jesus to come and eat.

'I have food enough for the moment,' Jesus replied, for He was still thinking about the woman's words and the implications of her faith in Messiah.

The disciples misunderstood what He meant and were shocked, for they then assumed that He had accepted some food from the Samaritan woman. 'My food,' Jesus continued, 'comes from God My father who sustains me while I do His will.'

That same evening, the Samaritan woman brought some of her friends from the town and asked if Jesus would speak to them. She had told them of His claim to be the Messiah.

Jesus spoke with them for some time while everyone else kept well away. After they had all gone back to the town, Jesus said to His disciples, 'The farmer sows his seed, watches for the new plants and then predicts when the harvest will take place. But I tell you, look at this field, the people who have just left. They are ripe and ready for harvesting. Whoever sowed the seeds of faith in them should rejoice as much as the one who will see the harvest of their faith. Both should rejoice together for one person sows and another man reaps. I am sending you, one day, into the fields of the people around you to harvest their faith. You did not sow the seeds but you will profit from their work.' The next morning more people came out of the nearby town to meet and listen to Jesus, and they begged Him to stay there so that they could hear Him teach and preach. In fact, He stayed there only two days more.

After He had left the people of the town, the friends of the Samaritan woman said to her, 'We believe in Him, not because of what you said but because we have heard Him for ourselves. Indeed He is the Messiah.'

The following day, Jesus suggested to Peter, James, and John that they should walk up the eastern slopes of the nearby Mount Gerizim. The four men set off and in the bright sunshine walked at a good pace. Jesus took the opportunity of talking about the events of the day before.

'Yesterday there were those among the Twelve and among my followers who were distressed about my actions. Indeed there were those who think that I was wrong and feel it quite strongly.

'The message that I bring is going to bring division for there are those who cannot and those who will not really listen to what is being said.

'Tradition has a good grip on many people and most people want to resist change. For the Pharisees to change would imply that they were wrong before, and that they will never admit. So you see there will be division, not total peace. Indeed a family of five will be divided three against two; fathers will disagree violently with their sons; mothers with their daughters, and mothers-in-law with daughters-in-law. The Good News of the Kingdom is that of love and peace but not everyone will accept citizenship in the Kingdom.'

As they reached the foothills and began to climb, the mist began to descend. The bright sunshine and the cloud gave an eerie effect, and as the disciples looked up it was as if Jesus were clothed in a dazzling white cloak. For a moment it seemed as if this were a religious experience; as if God were confirming for them that Jesus really was the Son of God. Peter's reaction was, as usual, impetuous. 'Let us build a cairn of stones to mark this place for God has revealed Himself to us,' he said to the others. Before they had a chance of doing anything, the mist lifted and Jesus was standing there. Peter and the disciples said nothing about this event.

When they returned to the camp, everything had been packed up and the followers were ready to continue their journey. They were anxious to cross the border into Judea and to put Samaria behind them. Upon reaching the border, they saw a crowd of people, including some teachers of the Law, arguing with the rest of the Twelve. When the people saw Jesus they ran to Him and greeted Him. Jesus asked, 'What is going on?'

A man in the crowd stepped forward. 'Teacher, I brought my son to you because he suffers from fits. Whenever the spirit attacks him, it throws him to the ground; he foams at the mouth, grinds his teeth and goes rigid all over. I asked your disciples to heal him but they could not.'

Jesus was disappointed with them but said, 'Bring the boy to me.' So they did. As the boy was brought forward, he had another fit and threw himself onto the ground and did all the things that his father had described. Jesus asked, 'How long has he been like this?'

'Ever since he was a child,' the boy's father replied. 'Many times he has been in dangerous situations near fire and water, and it is amazing that he has not been killed. Please have pity on him and heal him if you can!'

'Everything is possible to a man of faith,' Jesus said.

'I do have faith, sir, but perhaps not enough,' the man replied. 'Help me to have more.' By now the crowd was moving closer, aware that something was about to happen.

Jesus gave a command as if to a spirit. 'Come out of him.' The boy screamed and everyone was afraid. Then the boy lay still, as if dead.

'Is he dead?' asked someone on the edge of the crowd.

Jesus took the boy by the hand, helped him to sit up, and then stand up. Everyone was amazed and thrilled, particularly the boy's father. 'Thank you sir,' he said with tears streaming down his face. The crowd returned to their homes.

Then the camp followers moved off on the next stage of their journey. Those disciples who had failed were asking themselves what had gone wrong.

CHAPTER 3

Judea

IN THE small town of Ephraim, Jesus was invited by a farmer to stay with him, or at least come for the evening meal. Jesus agreed to attend the evening meal, and when Jesus and His disciples arrived, it was obvious that the farmer had invited many of his farming friends. As was the custom, other people gathered in the courtyard to listen to the guest speaker who would talk later on in the meal. Much of the casual conversation was about the coming harvest and what yield there might be.

Jesus, after the meal was over, began His teaching session. 'Your conversation is about corn and the yield from your crops. People, of course, need corn for bread but I am here to tell you that I am the Bread of Life. Anyone who accepts me will never be hungry.' There was a stunned silence.

'But how can you feed us without bread?' asked one of the guests. 'Are you going to provide manna from heaven like our ancestors in the wilderness centuries ago?'

'No,' replied Jesus. 'Our ancestors ate manna in the desert, but they died. I am the true bread from heaven. If anyone eats this bread, he will live for ever.'

Again there was a puzzled silence. 'But we cannot eat

you!' stated one guest, totally missing the point of what Jesus was saying. Some of the guests started talking amongst themselves, dismissing what Jesus was saying as ridiculous.

'I assure you,' Jesus continued, 'If you receive me into your whole lives, just as this bread enters your whole body, you will receive eternal life, everlasting life with God.'

Many of the guests, and some of those listening in the crowd, could not understand what Jesus meant and left the meal grumbling and disappointed. Jesus turned to His own disciples and challenged them. 'Is this teaching too hard for you? Does it make you want to give up and go home?'

Peter replied impulsively, 'Lord, to whom would we go? You have the words that tell us about eternal life. We know who you are and that your message is from God.'

'Thank you, Peter,' replied Jesus, 'but not all of you will believe in me to the end!' Jesus stayed a few days in Ephraim, and many came to accept Him as the Messiah before He and His followers moved on.

When they reached Bethel, another place of pilgrimage, they made camp, and Jesus and some of the disciples went into the town. Jesus's reputation was well known so it was not long before He was recognised. A teacher of the Law joined a small crowd of people who had gathered round Jesus listening to Him teaching about the Kingdom of God and God's offer of eternal life. At an appropriate moment, and in an attempt to get Jesus to admit His own guilt in breaking the Law, he asked, 'Is it true that you have come through Samaria and have talked to the people in that country?'

'Yes,' said Jesus, aware of what the man was trying to do.

'Is that not deliberately breaking the Law?' he continued.

'The offer of eternal life is for every one of God's children,'

Jesus replied.

'Teacher,' he went on, 'you talk about this eternal life. What must I do to receive such a wonderful gift?'

Jesus, as usual, asked him a question in return. 'You, sir, are a teacher also. What do the Scriptures say about what God wants from us in response to His gift of life? What is your interpretation?'

The man replied, 'To keep the commandments.'

'Yes,' said Jesus, and was about to turn away when the Teacher continued quickly, 'But which commandments?'

Jesus answered, 'Do not commit murder; do not commit adultery; do not steal; do not accuse anyone falsely; respect your mother and father, and love your neighbour as yourself.'

'But I have obeyed all these commandments,' persisted the Teacher, 'since I was a child! What more do I need to do?'

Jesus looked straight at him. 'If you want to receive this gift of eternal life, then go and sell all that you have, give the money to the poor and then come and follow me.'

The young man averted his eyes from Jesus. The challenge was too great for he was a rich man. He turned away sad and disappointed.

After more teaching, Jesus left the village and made His way to the site of Jacob's dream, a moment of pilgrimage. He and His followers spent some time in prayer and then returned to their camp site. While the men were eating their evening meal, Andrew asked Jesus, 'Is there no hope for the rich of this world, like that young man earlier today?'

Jesus replied, 'It is hard for the rich to enter the Kingdom of God.' When the disciples heard this they were completely amazed. One of them asked, 'Then who can be saved?'

'It is impossible for a man to achieve it, but not for God. You cannot buy nor earn your way into the Kingdom. Anyone carrying the baggage of wealth, power and position is unlikely to be willing to give them up and put God first in their lives.'

Then Peter said, 'Lord, we have given up everything and followed you. Will we receive this gift of eternal life?'

Jesus looked reassuringly at Peter. 'You can be sure that when God's Kingdom comes on earth, you, and everyone who has given up family, employment, wealth and position, will be given the gift of eternal life. But many who think that they will be the first to enter the Kingdom because of their wealth and standing in society will be disappointed. They may have to wait a long time. Similarly, those who think that they have no hope of entering because they have nothing left to offer will find themselves accepted and welcomed straight away.'

CHAPTER 4

Jerusalem

NEXT day, they struck camp and continued on their way to Jerusalem. The fields around them were being harvested, and Jesus wanted to be in the city for the Sabbath, the Day of Atonement and the Festival of Tabernacles. He and His followers approached the city as the Sabbath began. They came to the famous Pool of Bethzatha, near the Sheep Gate in the city walls. Here there were five porches, and it was a regular place for the sick, the lame, the blind, the deaf and the dumb to gather. It was believed that when the waters of the pool were disturbed by supernatural forces, then whoever managed to get into the pool first would be healed. There was a man there who had been paralysed for a long time, in fact for thirty-eight years he told the authorities later.

Jesus took pity and went to him. 'Do you want to be healed?'

'Yes sir,' replied the man, 'but I have no-one to help me into the pool when the waters are disturbed. I can never get there first!'

Jesus bent down and took the man's arm. He said to him, 'Get up, pick up your mat and go home.' To his amazement, the man found strength coming back into his legs as Jesus lifted him. He picked up his mat and started to walk slowly in the direction of his home. People who saw what had happened surrounded him and asked him all about it. A message reached some of the authorities and they came to see the man.

'Hey you,' one of them said. 'You are carrying your mat and it is already the Sabbath. You are breaking the law.' It sounded such a pathetic charge, but people were used to such things happening.

The man defended himself. 'The man who made me well told me to carry my mat,' he replied, and turned around as if he could point the man out.

'Who was the man who did this and told you to do that?' the enquirer persisted.

However, the man could not reply for he did not know who Jesus was, and by then Jesus had disappeared into the large crowds entering the city for the Festival.

Later on in the evening, when Jesus was worshipping in the Temple, the man saw Jesus and came to thank Him. Jesus told him, 'From now on live a new life. This is just the day for confessing your sins to God and making a new start to your life.'

Then the man, in all innocence, told the Temple Police and pointed out that it was this man who had healed him.

They approached Jesus, similarly not knowing who He was, and told Him that He must not do this sort of thing again on the Sabbath as it was against the Law.

Jesus looked at them and shook His head in sadness. 'My Father is always working and so must I,' He said, but they did not understand what He meant.

Instead He became a marked man and was watched to see what else He would do during the Festival.

Jesus noticed a young man, perhaps thirteen or fourteen years old, watching Him. He had noticed him at the Pool of Bethzatha earlier that evening. He looked at the young man and that seemed to encourage him. He came forward.

'I would like you to come home and meet my father and mother,' he said to Jesus. 'I have told them about what I saw you do at the Pool earlier this evening.'

'All right then,' said Jesus, and indicated to the other disciples who were with Him that he would go alone. The young man led Him from the Temple to the Upper City, past the house of Caiaphas the High Priest, beyond the stepped streets area, and on to a large two-storeyed house. As he entered the house, he called for his parents. They appeared from two different places and were somewhat embarrassed to find that they had a guest.

'This is the man I was telling you about,' said the young man to his parents.

'John Mark,' said his father with a tone that sounded like a reprimand, 'we were not ready for guests.' Then, turning to Jesus, he said, 'Sir, you are welcome. Please forgive our lack of preparation.' Then he introduced his wife. 'This is my wife Anna, and I am Kenan. You have met our only son John Mark.'

Jesus acknowledged their welcome, and then said, 'My name is Jesus,' which sounded strange for He was so used to being known by most people whom He met.

'Oh yes! The miracle worker!' Kenan said, somewhat formally. 'Please come and sit in the courtyard. It is still warm enough and we can offer you some refreshment.' He led the way, and the young man, ever attentive to Jesus, walked with Jesus. When they were seated, he went on, 'Now our son seems to think he saw you heal someone at the Pool.' It was said as a statement, but Jesus knew that it was really a question.

'Sadly there are so many people today who lack understanding, particularly of matters of the mind and paralysis. On a number of occasions during my ministry, I have had the opportunity of helping, healing if you would prefer, a number of people with these similar conditions,' Jesus answered.

'Your ministry?' Kenan replied by taking up Jesus's words.

'Yes,' replied Jesus. 'I was sent by My Father to teach people about God's Kingdom of Love, to call people to repentance and to make a new start to their lives, and to show God's love through a healing ministry.' Jesus looked straight at Kenan.

Kenan was taken aback by the honesty and conviction of Jesus, and was almost mesmerised by His eyes. It was as if Jesus could see straight into him. 'I am not sure that I really understand what you are implying. If you mean that your ministry is from God, then are you implying that you are the Messiah?'

John Mark was wrapped up in the conversation and listening to every word of Jesus, and already totally convinced as to who Jesus really was. 'Of course he is,' he said to his father.

'Such is the innocent faith of youth,' said Kenan.

'Amen to that,' replied Jesus.

'But surely the authorities would recognise you and accept you?' Kenan persisted. Before Jesus had an opportunity to reply, Kenan went on, 'No, I suppose they would not. They would be more likely to see you as a threat.' Jesus was impressed by his perceptive understanding. He let him continue without interruption. 'I believe in God, but I could never become a strict Jew, whether Pharisee, Saducee, Essene, Zealot or any other group, accepting all their interpretations of the Law, their strict code of conduct and their narrow-minded understanding of the Sabbath.'

Jesus was even more impressed. Here was a man who thought things out for himself. He began to talk about the Law and His interpretation of it. He talked about God's personal love and what faith could achieve. He talked about having a personal relationship with God and the gift of eternal life. In one sense it was extraordinary to talk in this way with someone whom he had just met, and yet he knew that this was the right place and the right time.

'He has so many followers,' John Mark interrupted. 'Father, may I become one of His followers?'

Both Kenan and Jesus smiled in admiration. 'You are too young,' his father replied. 'Perhaps in a few years time we can consider it again.' Turning to Jesus, he said, 'would you be gracious enough to share our meal?' Jesus accepted. Kenan continued, 'In some extraordinary way I feel I have known you for such a long time!'

The meal was a real blessing, and Jesus accepted the invitation to stay the night. Conversation went on long after John Mark had gone to bed, and the boy was sad to hear that when he did wake in the morning Jesus had already left. Kenan's farewell was accompanied by the words, 'My house is your house if you ever need it.' It was an offer that was soon to be accepted.

CHAPTER 5

Bethany

JESUS found the camp site after He had spent time in the Temple praying. He told the followers that He was going to Bethany to visit some friends. When He reached the village, He asked for the house of Simon. He followed the directions given Him, and it was not long before Jesus was welcomed into the home and family of Simon.

'This is the man I told you about,' he said to his wife and household. 'He healed me of leprosy!' and without any inhibitions he embraced Jesus out of sheer joy. 'Go to our neighbours and tell Lazarus and his sisters that Jesus is here.' He was so excited.

Soon all three came and were introduced to Jesus.

Mary and Martha, the two sisters of Lazarus, were so grateful to Jesus, and told Him of the home coming of the men and the telling of the story of their journeys. A mid-day meal was prepared and this provided a natural break in the conversations, for everyone wanted to know about Jesus and His ministry, and Martha especially seemed to hang upon His every word. It was a good day, but Jesus was tired by so much talking. When He rose to leave He was only able to do so with the promise that He would come back the next day, this time to the home of Lazarus.

On His way back to camp, Jesus took time to be quiet and to pray, to reflect on His new friends in the city and in the village, and with the feeling that they would all have an important part to play in His future ministry.

The next day He kept His promise and arrived at the home of Lazarus in good time for the evening meal. Mary and Martha were busy preparing the meal, but time and time again Mary came into the room where Jesus, Lazarus, and Simon were talking. She was so fascinated by Jesus and His way of talking that every time she came into the room to prepare the table she sat and listened herself. Martha, her sister, became more and more agitated so that eventually she interrupted Jesus while He was speaking.

'Excuse me, sir,' she said to Jesus. Then, turning to Lazarus, said, 'don't you care that my sister has left me to do all the work? Tell her to come and help me!'

Jesus spoke before Lazarus had the opportunity. 'Martha, Martha, you are upset about so many little things. There is only one thing that really matters and that is our relationship with God. However understandable your concern about the meal, your sister Mary is searching for that faith, that relationship.' There was silence, and Martha returned to the kitchen, though Mary followed soon after.

Jesus and His new friends enjoyed their evening together and talked until late about the Kingdom of God.

The next day, Jesus took Peter, Andrew, James, and John to visit Bethlehem. To be so near to His birthplace and not to visit it would have been unnatural. As they walked along the road, Jesus talked to them about the future.

'It seems strange to think about death when I am about to visit the place of my birth. Soon you will have to face the greatest challenge of your lives. I shall eventually be arrested and executed, and there are those who will seek to harm you because you are my disciples. I will pray that God my Father will give you courage and strength to go on. But have no fear, I have overcome the world, and the ultimate victory will be mine.' Then He told them a story to encourage them.

'In a town, there was a certain judge. He neither feared God nor bothered about his fellow man. There was also a certain widow in that town who kept coming to him demanding her rights and asking for his help. For a long time the judge refused to listen to her and help her. However, in time, he gave in. "I do not care about God or my fellow men," he said, "but this widow is making a nuisance of herself. I will see that she gets her rights! If I do not, then she will wear me out and give me no peace!"

'So,' said Jesus, 'go on demanding help from God in heaven in those difficult times and He will give you the help that you will need.'

'Similarly, suppose one of you went to a friend's house at midnight and knocked on his door until he was awake and answered it. You might say to him, "Friend, let me borrow three loaves of bread. A friend of mine on a journey has just arrived and I have no food for him." Suppose your friend should answer, "Go away. I and my family are in bed and everything is locked up. I am not getting up at this time of night to help you." However, if he realises that you will go on asking, then, friend or no friend, he will get up and give you what you need. So I say to you, go on asking God for what you need.'

When they arrived at Bethlehem, Jesus told them the stories that His mother had told Him. He talked of the census, the packed town, the accommodation in the stable of an inn and of His birth in such surroundings. There was no way of knowing which inn was the right one, but those with Jesus all took in something of the atmosphere of the town and its significance for Jesus. They stayed the night in Bethlehem.

The following day, He asked the disciples with Him to go back to Jerusalem in time for the Festival of Tabernacles, and to see that His followers built Shelters on the hillside as part of that festival. He promised to join them later.

Jesus spent much of the time talking with people, hearing stories of the past, including some dreadful accounts of Herod's violent outrage on the city when tiny children were massacred. He spent much time in prayer and meditation sitting outside the town and looking at it.

Jesus returned to Jerusalem after four days, about half way through the Festival. He went to the Temple and was soon involved in teaching sessions for people flocked to hear Him. He had made no announcement of His coming, but His reputation had gone before Him and as soon as someone said, 'Jesus is in the Temple', there were those who came to listen. There were many different views held about Him. Some said that He was a good man, some called Him 'The Miracle Worker', some dared to say that He claimed to be the Messiah. However, much of what was said was done so in whispers for there were strong rumours that the Pharisees had instructed the Temple Police to arrest Him whenever they could.

Those sent by the Pharisees to listen to His teaching were genuinely impressed and amazed at His knowledge and ability as a teacher. 'How is it that He knows so much and yet has never had any official training?'

That afternoon in the Temple, aware of the Temple Police and the representatives of the Pharisees, Jesus said, 'What I teach is not my own teaching but it comes from God and I am His instrument. Whoever is willing to do the will of God and to come to serve Him will know for themselves whether what I teach is from God or on my own authority. A person who speaks for himself is only really interested in receiving the glory from those he draws around him. But the one who draws people to God and away from himself is the true teacher of God's message, and there is nothing false in his teaching.'

Some in the crowd asked one another, 'Isn't this the man wanted by the authorities? Yet they are here and doing nothing to stop Him. Do you think that they know He is the Messiah, or do you think they are waiting for Him to perform some more miracles?'

Some suggested that the arrest would take place on the Sabbath when Jesus would be provoked into breaking the Law. Indeed someone, probably one of those seeking His arrest, asked Him about the healing of the paralysed man at the Pool. 'Teacher, is it right to heal on the Sabbath?'

Jesus replied, 'Do not judge by external standards but by true standards. What is right is right, and what is wrong is wrong, whatever day it may be. Moses and our ancestors taught us to circumcise our sons on the Sabbath. That is work and yet it is considered all right on the Sabbath because of the nature of the act. I enabled someone to walk again, and on the Sabbath. Surely that too is good and should not be considered to be breaking the Law?'

Those sent to arrest Him were so unsure of themselves, and afraid of the attitude of the crowd, that they let Him carry on. In fact, Jesus challenged them indirectly.

'Soon I shall leave you,' continued Jesus, 'and you will not be able to find me because you cannot go where I am going. So use the opportunity of listening to me while you can. The time is coming when I shall be arrested by the authorities, condemned to death and killed.'

Those listening to Him did not understand and thought that He had gone too far. 'No-one is going to kill you because of your teaching and miracles! If you think so, then you must have a devil inside you!'

When this was reported to the authorities, they asked, 'where is He going so that we cannot find Him?' but no-one knew the answer.

On the last day of the Festival, Jesus was again in the Temple. It was hot, and many were thirsty. Jesus took advantage of that moment and said, 'Whoever is thirsty should come to me and drink until he is fully satisfied. Even the scriptures promise that whoever believes in me will have "streams of life giving water within him".' This reference was to the Messiah and the coming of the Holy Spirit, but those listening did not understand. Once again there were those who wanted to acclaim Him as the Messiah, but others thought Him to be a Prophet.

Someone in the crowd, this time a genuine seeker after the truth and probably someone normally rejected by society, asked Him, 'Can anyone receive such a blessing?'

Jesus answered him by telling this story. 'One day, two men came into the Temple to pray. One was a Pharisee and one was a tax collector, a collaborator. The Pharisee stood on his own, away from ordinary people, and prayed aloud, "I thank you God that you have made me different from the ordinary people, especially from people like this tax collector. I am not greedy or dishonest; I am not an adulterer or a cheat. I fast two days a week and give away one tenth of my income as the Law demands." The tax collector was not even conscious of other people around him. He did not even lift his head but beat his chest in repentance. "God in heaven," he said, "have pity on me, a sinner." I tell you it was the tax collector who went to his home having been put right with God, his sins forgiven, because of the sincerity of his confession. For every one who humbles himself will be lifted up but those who think themselves to be important in the eyes of God will be brought to their knees.'

As Jesus was walking away from the Temple, with some of the Twelve who had joined Him there, He saw a man who was blind. He found out afterwards that he had been blind from birth. The man was begging for money. Jesus stopped and talked with him. 'I can offer you something far more valuable,' He said to the man. 'I can make you see.' The man asked Jesus to help him see. Jesus spat on the ground and made a little mud. Then He rubbed the mud onto the man's eyes and said, 'Now go and wash in the Pool of Siloam.' The man found his way to the Pool and, sure enough, as soon as he washed the mud from his eyes he could see.

The story of this healing spread quickly, and the authorities heard of it too. They sent representatives to verify what had happened and to interrogate the man. Then they tried to discredit Jesus, but without success. The simple man stuck to his story. 'I know little about this man,' he said. 'What I do know is this. I was blind and now I can see!'

On the way back to camp, one of the Twelve asked Jesus, 'if that man was born blind, whose sin was responsible for his blindness, his own or his parents?'

Jesus replied, 'His blindness has nothing to do with sin.

115

God does not punish babies. However, this healing has now been used by God my Father so that you and others may be aware of the power of God.'

CHAPTER 6

Jericho

AFTER the festival, Jesus spent time with His followers, but also with His friends in Bethany. When He was about to leave and continue His ministry in Jericho, Mary, the sister of Lazarus, asked Him not to leave. 'My brother is far from well,' she said to Jesus, 'and I would feel easier in my mind if you were here. Please stay?' Jesus tried to explain to her that He felt guided to go to Jericho, and assured her that Lazarus would be well.

So Jesus set off on the notorious road to Jericho with His entire band of followers. As they came to the outskirts of the city they noticed a blind man sitting by the roadside and begging. When he heard the noise of a crowd of people passing by he asked, 'what is happening?'

Someone replied, 'Jesus, the Miracle worker, has come to Jericho.'

Immediately the man shouted out, 'Jesus, have pity on me!'

Some of those in the group of followers told him to be quiet. However, he shouted even louder, 'Jesus, have pity on me!'

Jesus heard his shouts and told the group to stop. 'Bring the man here,' He ordered. When the man was brought to Him, He asked the man, 'What do you want me to do for you?'

The man replied, 'Sir, I want to be able to see again.'

'What is your name?' Jesus asked.

'Bartimaus, sir, son of Timaeus,' the man replied.

Jesus said, 'Then be happy, Bartimaus! Your faith in me has been rewarded. Open your eyes and see once more!' Jesus laid His hands on him, and when the man opened his eyes again he could see. The man was so wonderfully happy that he followed Jesus and His disciples as they entered Jericho. He was praising God aloud and he told everyone he could about what Jesus had done. The group set up camp on the other side of the city.

The next day, Jesus entered the city, probably the oldest city in the world, and began to teach those who would listen. Every day He did this and He became so popular that crowds of people would line the streets when He went in and out of the city. One day, as He was leaving the city, cheering crowds had gathered along the way. Zacchaeus, a rich man, the chief tax collector for the city, a man hated because of his job as well as for being considered to be a collaborator, heard the noise of the crowd and came out of his house to see Jesus. He was a small man and tried to elbow his way to the front of the crowd in order to see Him. Because of who he was, no-one would let him through. So he did the next best thing, ran ahead of the crowd and climbed a sycamore tree by the roadside, knowing that Jesus would pass that way.

When Jesus reached the place where Zacchaeus was clinging on to the tree, Jesus spoke to him directly. 'Come on down. I would like to come to your home.' Zacchaeus climbed down as quickly as he could. People in the crowd were amazed by what Jesus was going to do.

'Does He realise who Zacchaeus is?' they asked. 'Surely He would not go and eat with a collaborator?'

Jesus, however, knew exactly who he was and what he was

doing. Zacchaeus gave orders for a meal to be prepared for Jesus, and was overwhelmed by the fact that Jesus had come to his house. They talked for a long time, and at the end Zacchaeus was convinced that Jesus was the Messiah. So much so that he wanted to make amends for his corrupt life. 'Sir,' he said, 'I will give half of what I own to the poor. If I have cheated anyone, I will pay back four times as much!'

Jesus responded. As He left the house, He said to the people at the door, 'Today salvation has come to this home. God has sent me on a mission to the Jews, and this man is a true Jew. He has responded to God's call for repentance for I was sent not only to call the righteous to make a new beginning to their lives, but I was sent especially to seek out those society believes to be "lost".'

The next day, Jesus continued the same theme. There were many tax collectors and other society rejects in the crowd. Already some Pharisees in the crowd were complaining about their presence and the fact that Jesus had eaten a meal with Zacchaeus. So Jesus told them the story of a shepherd.

'Suppose one of you is hired as a shepherd and has a hundred sheep in his flock. If he loses one of them, what does he do?

'He makes sure that the ninety-nine are in safe pasture or a sheepfold and then goes off to look for the one that is lost. He goes on searching until he finds it. When he finds it, he is so happy that he carries it home on his shoulders. He is so relieved that in the evening he calls on his friends and neighbours to tell them what had happened. Then he celebrates with them his joy of finding the lost sheep. In the same way, I assure you, there is more rejoicing in heaven over one sinner who repents than over the ninety and nine people who do not need to repent.'

In order to re-enforce His message, He went on, 'Or suppose a woman who has ten silver coins on her dowry chain loses one of them. What does she do? She lights a lamp, sweeps her house very carefully and looks everywhere until she finds the coin. When she finds it she calls on her friends and neighbours to tell them her good news. 'I am so happy,' she will say. 'I lost a coin from my dowry and I was so worried. But I searched for it and eventually found it.' Then she too will celebrate with her friends. I tell you again there will be rejoicing in heaven each time someone who was considered to be lost to God turns again to God and is found.'

So Jesus spent several months in the city and the neighbouring villages, teaching, preaching, and healing.

One day He was answering questions from the Jewish community when a man asked Him about foreigners and God's gift of eternal life. 'Will people like the Samaritans be offered this gift?' he challenged.

Jesus asked, 'Is there a lawyer among you?'

'Yes,' replied one man.

'What is the law about love?' Jesus asked.

'That we must love God with all our whole selves, and our neighbours as ourselves,' he replied.

Jesus knew well of the hatred that these Jews had for the Samaritans and, for that matter, for all foreigners. So He told them this story. 'One day there was a man travelling that notorious road from Jerusalem to Jericho. On the way, he was attacked by thieves, stripped of his clothes as well as his purse, beaten up, and left to die. Now it so happened that a priest was making that same journey at a similar time. When he came to the man, though he was concerned for him, he was probably more concerned about the consequences of touching him. If he were dead and he touched him, then the priest would have to observe days of ritual cleansing. He could not afford that, so he walked on and left the man where he was.

'Soon afterwards, a second man came along that same part of the road. This man was an expert in the Law, and a man who had heard many stories of criminal activities. He knew that robbers often used decoys to lure wealthy people to their death. He was not going to take the risk. So he too went on passed the man.

'A third man came along the road, travelling on a donkey. He was a foreigner, all of whom, as you well know, are hated by the Jews. Yet immediately he saw the man, he stopped, got off his donkey, bathed the man's wounds as best he could, bandaged him up and then laid the man on his donkey and led the donkey to the nearest inn. Then he paid the innkeeper to look after the man until he was well enough to get home. 'If the final cost is more than this,' he said, 'I will pay the rest the next time I go past your inn.'

'Now,' said Jesus, 'which of the three men in the story do you think was the real neighbour to the injured man?'

'The one who stopped and cared for him,' the lawyer replied.

'Yes, of course,' said Jesus, 'you are correct. Now go and do the same. Be a good neighbour to anyone in need. God's love is for all, and His gifts are for all.'

On another occasion, Jesus taught, 'I am the good shepherd. I know and care for my sheep. They know me and recognise my voice. I lead them to good pastures and they follow me because they trust me. They will not follow anyone else because they do not know their voice.

'As a good shepherd, I sit at the entrance of the sheepfold making sure that they are safe, for no wild animal will get past me. Any man who climbs over the walls of the sheepfold is a thief and will be dealt with as such.

'The good shepherd is ready to die protecting his sheep if necessary. The hired man runs away at the first signs of danger, for example when a wolf attacks. I will protect my sheep whatever the cost.' He left the crowd in no doubt that God cared for everyone.

Soon after this, Jesus received an urgent message to say that Lazarus was critically ill. He was requested to return immediately. To His followers' surprise, Jesus stayed on in Jericho for two more days before giving the orders to strike camp and go back to Jerusalem. In answer to their obvious concern, He said, 'Do not worry. he will not die. The time is not yet right for me to return to Jerusalem.' However they were not reassured. So it was two days later they all returned to the Mount of Olives near Jerusalem.

CHAPTER 7

Back to Bethany

WHEN they reached the Mount of Olives, the followers made camp amongst all the others visiting Jerusalem for the Passover Festival. During the evening, a messenger arrived from Bethany with a message for Jesus. It was from Mary, the sister of Lazarus, to say that her brother had died. There was an embarrassed silence around the camp as the news spread. Jesus said reassuringly, 'Our friend Lazarus is asleep and I will go and wake him.' Jesus set off, and Thomas called to the Twelve to go with Him.

When Jesus arrived, He found all the trappings for a funeral. Martha, the sister of Mary and Lazarus, came to meet Him and said, 'Lord, if you had been here, my brother would not have died.'

'Your brother will live,' said Jesus confidently.

'I know that he will live again at the resurrection,' she replied, assuming that that was what Jesus meant.

Jesus said to her, 'I am the one who brings resurrection and life. Whoever believes in me will live for ever. Do you believe that?' He challenged.

Martha responded quietly, 'Yes Lord.' Then she went into the house to tell Mary, her sister, 'The Master is here,' she said. When Mary heard this, she hurried out to greet Jesus. The mourners in the house followed, presuming that Mary had suddenly decided to go to the bier where Lazarus was lying. When Mary met Jesus she said the same thing as her sister. 'Lord, if you had been here, my brother would not have died.' She wept, and the mourners wept with her.

'Where have you put him?' Jesus asked.

'Out in the garden near the tomb,' she replied. 'His body was already beginning to smell.'

Jesus went out into the garden, followed by the family, the mourners, the Twelve, and the friends and neighbours that were present. Someone had already started to prepare the body of Lazarus for burial by binding strips of cloth like bandages around him. Jesus, to the astonishment of everyone, started to undo the bandages. He called for washing items. When Mary brought these things, He washed Lazarus's face and arms.

'I told Martha that your brother is in a coma, like a deep sleep.' Jesus then laid His hands on Lazarus and in a loud voice shouted, 'In the name of God, wake up!' There was a tense silence for a few minutes. Then Mary gave a sudden intake of breath. She noticed that her brother's eye lids moved. She clung to Jesus for support.

Minutes later, Lazarus opened his eyes, tried to focus on Jesus, and moved his head. There was now a huge intake of breath from everyone else, and one of the women said, 'Jesus has brought Lazarus back from the dead!' Mary and Martha now came to Lazarus, helped him to sit up, and encouraged everyone to go back into the house so they could wash him all over and get him dressed.

When some of the mourners returned to Jerusalem, they were

eager to tell their story. Lazarus was well known, not only in the village of Bethany but in the city as well. 'Jesus brought Lazarus back from the dead!' they stated confidently. Rumours travelled quickly, and it was not long before they reached the offices of the High Priest, Caiaphas. 'He is back,' they stated, 'and this time it is claimed that He has brought Lazarus back from the dead! They are now flocking to hear Jesus teach,' said one of the officials.

After much consultation, it was suggested that Lazarus should be killed, and the people told he never had been raised from the dead, so ending these rumours. But it had to be done in a way that would give the impression that Jesus had failed and that His supporters had made up the story. It was also agreed that Jesus would have to be arrested and put to death in order to maintain peace at this year's Passover celebrations.

Someone who heard this and knew what was to happen found one of the disciples of Jesus and warned him. This disciple, Judas, in turn warned Jesus and persuaded Him to go to visit friends in Ephraim for a few days, and then return when the Passover Festival began. 'They would not dare to arrest you then with the whole city full of pilgrims,' he stated confidently.

So Jesus and His disciples set off on the Damascus Road for Ephraim, a village just beyond Bethel. They stayed with friends there, but Jesus was anxious to return to Jerusalem. The final challenge awaited Him there.

As the time for Passover drew near, Jesus joined other pilgrims making their way to Jerusalem. As He caught a glimpse of the sun glinting on the golden-coated roof of the Holy of Holies, part of the Temple which dominated everything, even the city itself, He remembered His days of temptation in the wilderness. Temptation would now return with greater force, and He prayed that He would be strong enough to resist it again.

PART THREE

FROM

BETHANY

TO

GLORY

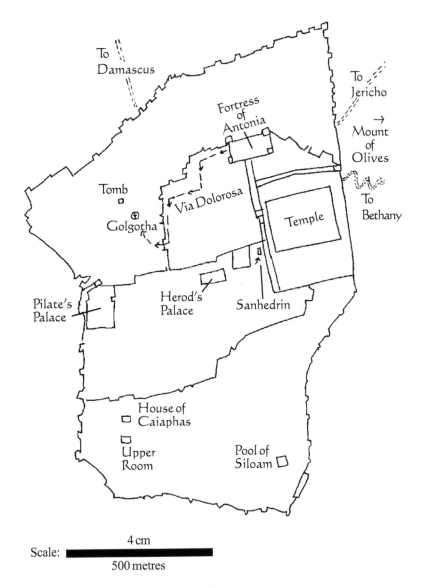

CHAPTER 1

SUNDAY

ONCE the dawn chorus had ceased, there was a short period of stillness where every tiny sound echoed. There was a peace which was as refreshing as the gentle cool breeze that sprang up as the first light of the sun ushered in the day. Then came the crescendo of noise from crickets, wild dogs, and all the other creatures that lived in the wilderness. Jesus sat still in the semi-darkness on top of the hill, looking at the changing scene as the rays of the sun played on the roofs of the city of Jerusalem. This moment of peace and new beginning would never come again for Him. Here was the true beginning of the end.

'If this really is what must happen, Father, then so be it. I will be obedient to the end,' Jesus said aloud. He thought and prayed in the pregnant atmosphere of this new day.

The women were busy in the camp preparing the breakfast while the men were coming to terms with the fact that it was getting light and the great day had arrived. Peter, having wakened, washed and tidied his appearance, wandered out of the camp, gazed up to the hills behind for any sign of Jesus. He knew that Jesus would be up there somewhere. To a certain extent he was frustrated because he wanted to know what was happening. He was confident that Jesus had made all sorts of detailed preparations for this day but for some reason He had not shared it with the Twelve.

Passover time was a great experience, particularly for those pilgrims who made their way to Jerusalem. Many had arrived during the last four days. The hillsides were strewn with camp sites and would soon be throbbing with the pulse of people getting ready for a festival day. Half a million people were here for the Festival! Fifty thousand lambs had to be slaughtered. This was no ordinary day in the life of the capital city. There was an excited atmosphere even at this time in the morning. Word had got round that Jesus was to be at the Festival, so there was, for some, an added excitement, but for the authorities there was nervous anticipation. There were those who were anxious to see Jesus, to see what healings He would perform and to hear Him teach and preach. On the other hand there were the Jewish authorities anxious to stamp out this prophet and His following in order to avoid trouble with the Roman officials. An already charged atmosphere in the city was about to explode.

Meanwhile, Jesus had returned to His host's home in Bethany, shared a light meal with them and prepared His apparel for the day ahead. When He was ready, He asked a blessing on that home and said farewell. He made His way out of the village and across the hillside towards the camp where all His immediate followers would be waiting.

After greeting the Twelve, He sat down and started to give orders, like a king going into battle. 'We shall go first of all to the village of Bethage and then down the Mount of Olives, past the Gardens of Gethsemane, through the Kidron valley, and on up to the Lion Gate a short distance from the Golden Gate of the city.' He turned and looked at Philip and

Nathaniel. 'Go into Bethage ahead of us. At the outskirts of the village, you will see a donkey's colt, one that has never been ridden before, tied up and waiting to be collected. Untie it and bring it to me. If anyone challenges you, then simply repeat these words, "The Master needs it", and they will leave you alone.'

The two set off immediately. Jesus held up His hands to announce to the camp to be silent for He was going to pray. He asked a blessing on them all, and on all that would take place that day. Then He turned and led the disciples and His followers towards Bethage.

Philip and Nathaniel never doubted for a minute that what Jesus had said would happen. Sure enough, as they entered the village, there was the colt. As they were untying him, someone came out of a nearby house and challenged them.

'What are you doing untying that colt?' he said.

'The Master needs him,' said Philip in a bold voice. It sounded like a pre-arranged password, for immediately the man turned away and went back into the house. They led the donkey towards the top of the Mount of Olives and waited for Jesus to arrive. Nathaniel, looking at the donkey, took off his outer garment, folded it and laid it across the donkey's back.

When Jesus arrived, what had started out as a group of people walking along the path in order to go to the city had become a procession. It was already mid-morning and there were plenty of people on the hillside. Jesus thanked the two disciples, noting Nathaniel's kindness, put His leg over the donkey and sat there as regal as anyone could be. Philip, who had not let go of the donkey's rope, now pulled him forward for the journey down the hill. The colt was reluctant. The procession moved forward slowly. Jesus then paused at the highest point, looking down on the city with the roof of the Temple reflecting the golden rays of the sunshine. The Twelve, and everyone else around Jesus, stopped, uncertain what they should do. Jesus seemed strangely quiet, almost lost in a world of His own. Then they noticed tears welling up into His eyes. He spoke softly, more to himself than to anyone else. 'Oh Jerusalem, if only you had realised the Truth of God, what a day this could have been. I could have brought you peace and freedom. Your rejection of me will bring you far worse consequences than you can imagine. Soon this wonderful sight will be no more. Within a generation your enemies will destroy you, and the beauty and colour with which you are clothed today will be replaced by sackcloth and ashes.'

At that moment, some cheering began not far away. A group of people from one of the nearby camp sites had seen and recognised Jesus. They were rushing to see Him and touch Him. Suddenly the atmosphere changed. The donkey, disturbed by the sudden noise, moved forward and the whole procession followed. Others on the hillsides heard the noise and came to see what was happening. News spread quickly, and people grabbed anything they could to wave. Branches were torn off nearby trees. Some were just waved in the air, while others were laid on the rough path like a matting. Some people, rather overcome with enthusiasm, even threw their outer garments over the branches. A crowd attracts a crowd, and before long the path was blocked by people anxious to see who was the centre of attention, and then, finding out that it was Jesus, wanted to touch Him. Philip and Nathaniel had great difficulty in keeping to the path, but going down hill gave them a little added momentum. Then some people began to sing and chant. 'God bless the king! God bless the king! God bless the one who comes in the name of our God! God bless the one who brings us peace!' The disciples had never seen anything like this before, and they too got caught up in the euphoria of the occasion. This contagion of joy spread rapidly and, as the masses crossed the Kidron Valley and approached the Golden Gate, the noise could be heard throughout the city. It was now late morning and very hot.

By the city gate, a group of Pharisees blocked the way. The crowd slowed automatically. An atmosphere of apprehension spread from the front to the back of the crowd and the crescendo of noise abated.

'Command your disciples to cease this blasphemy,' the Pharisees demanded. 'You are a Rabbi, not a King! All this is an offence to God!'

The first confrontation of the Festival had begun. Quietly, and without any challenging intonation in His voice, Jesus answered them. 'I'll tell you this, if these people keep quiet, the very stones in these walls will burst out in cheering!' After a moment of stunned silence from the Pharisees, the crowds started cheering again and the human wave surged forward once more. Through this gate of the city and on to the Temple, Jesus and His army of supporters flowed like a human river.

When Jesus reached the Temple, He dismounted from the donkey in a pathway below the court and entered the first court of the Temple, the Court of the Gentiles. It was more like a market square, with pens for the animals, tables with bird cages on, and tables for the money changers. The noise of the animals and the hucksters, the hubbub of conversation, the smell of animal dung and sweaty human beings, filled the air. Add to that the atmosphere of carnage and the occasional shrieks from the animals, and it would be difficult to think of something less like a place of worship. Jesus was incensed.

Turning on the Pharisees who were standing and watching, He said forcefully, 'You dare to accuse me of blasphemy! This whole scene is a blasphemy. This is the House of God, and you have turned it into a den for thieves. It is meant to be a place for prayer, and you have allowed it to be come a noisy market place.' Then, without warning, He grabbed a whip from one of the herdsmen and cracked it in the air. Suddenly all eyes were turned upon Him. In quick succession He opened the animal pens and released the animals; He opened the bird cages and released the birds; He turned over the money-changers tables so that coins went everywhere, and began to drive out the merchants, cracking the whip, as if they were the animals.

It all happened so suddenly that no one reacted quickly enough to do anything about it. Then the shocked Temple police and stewards woke out of their temporary stupor. Some chased after the animals while others tried to stop the people who were scrambling in the dust and dirt for the money. There was chaos! Jesus turned His back on all this confusion. He walked out of the Temple, back to and through the Golden Gate leaving behind Him the stench of the animals and the stench from the greediness of humanity.

The Gethsemane Gardens were a welcome relief in the heat of the day. The peace and quiet, marginally disturbed by the noise of the city, and the cool shade, enabled everyone to doze and some to sleep. Jesus, lying on the ground, contemplated what had happened.

In the late afternoon, Jesus returned to the city and to the Temple. There was a calmer atmosphere now. However, He was soon surrounded by people clamouring for healing, including the blind and the crippled. He talked with them, prayed with them, and many were healed. The Temple Police had tracked His every move this time, as a result of the morning's disruption and their desire to arrest Him. Word had been sent to the Jewish authorities, and some Pharisees were watching Jesus at work, but from a distance. People who were healed, shouted with joy, 'Praise to King David's Son!' Some of the crowd took up the chant. The Pharisees were angry and shouted to Jesus.

'Do you hear what they are singing?' they challenged.

'Indeed I do,' replied Jesus. 'They are like children who have been given a wonderful toy. Their delight is real, genuine and innocent, like perfect praise.'

The Pharisees realised there was no way that they could arrest Jesus at this time. 'You see, we have lost control for the moment,' they said to one another. 'They are all following Him now!'

Jesus left the Temple and made His way back to Bethany to spend the evening with His friends.

CHAPTER 2

MONDAY

THE following morning, after a slow start to the day, Jesus and His followers once again made their way towards Jerusalem. This time, Jesus led them around the Mount of Olives until they crossed over to the Jericho road. They passed a well-known landmark, a giant fig tree, that had stood there for years. As they came near to it, one of the disciples remarked on how green were the leaves and how healthy the tree looked. Jesus inspected the tree, found no figs forming on it, and said, 'No-one will ever eat figs from this tree again. On the outside it seems all right, but it has all the marks of disease and decay on the inside.'

He was interrupted by some men who came to Him on the road. 'Master, we have come to warn you. We heard last night that Herod has sent some men to trap and kill you. Please go somewhere else today.'

'Thank you,' replied Jesus, 'but no. You can tell that old fox that I have work to do today, and tomorrow, here in Jerusalem. This is the right place for me to die.' They moved on and, as they came in view of the city, Jesus stopped. 'Oh Jerusalem, Jerusalem, how often I have wanted to protect you like a hen with her chicks, but you would not let me. Instead you have killed the prophets and stoned others whom

God has sent. Like that fig tree, you look lovely on the outside but inside you are rotten. The day will come when the Temple will be abandoned, the city will be destroyed, and you will wish that I were there to help you.'

Jesus entered the city through the Water Gate and made His way to the Temple once more. As He entered the Court of the Gentiles, some people came to Him asking for His help. As on previous occasions He talked with them, prayed with them, and healed some of them. Afterwards He sat down and prepared himself for a teaching session. Some of the senior priests, some lawyers, and some rabbis, as well as representatives of the Jewish authorities, who had been watching Jesus, came over to Him. They asked Him, 'By what authority do you do these things? Who gave you the right to teach here?'

Jesus answered with a question, conscious of the group of people that had now gathered around them. 'I will ask you just one question in return? If you can answer my question, then I will answer yours.' He paused, and there was an atmosphere of anticipation. 'Do you remember John, nicknamed the Baptist? Where did John's authority come from? Was it from God or from man?'

That group of listeners, including those representatives of the authorities, went into a huddle in order to find the right answer. They were well aware of the crowd that had gathered. There was a good deal of feeling still about the martyrdom of John by Herod, and they were afraid of what the people might do if they said that John was just a man and not a prophet, as was widely believed.

'What shall we say? If we say "from God", then they will accuse us of not believing in Him. If we say "from man", then they will turn on us.' After a few minutes, they turned again to Jesus. 'We cannot answer your question,' one of them said.

'Therefore I will not answer your question,' Jesus replied, much to the amusement of the crowd.

Someone in the crowd asked Him, 'They never accepted John. Why don't they believe you either?'

Jesus replied with this story. 'Once upon a time there was a man, a visitor to this country, who planted a vineyard, erected a fence round it, dug out pits for the winepress, and built a watch tower for guards to watch out for thieves. Then he rented out the vineyard to tenants and went back home. When it was time for the grapes to be harvested, he sent his representative to receive his share of the profits. However, the tenants beat him up and sent him back to his employer empty-handed as a warning.

'The owner sent someone else and the same thing happened. A third employee was sent, and this one they beat to death. In time, the owner only had one person to send and that was his own dear son. So he sent him with the conviction that at least they would respect his son and do as they had agreed at their tenancy and send him the harvest dues. When the tenants saw the son and realised who he was, they said, 'This is the owner's son. If we kill him, then we shall inherit the vineyard by right.' So they seized the son, killed him, and threw his body out of the vineyard.'

'Now what will the owner do?' Jesus continued. 'He will have those tenants arrested, convicted of murder, and then he will bring in other tenants. I come to you as God's representative.' He stopped and looked at those representatives of the authorities still at the edge of the crowd. They were angry and wanted to arrest Jesus because it was obvious that He had told this story against them. However they were afraid of the people, and so they went away.

There were some Greek speaking Jews who knew only a little Hebrew, who were visiting Jerusalem for the Festival. One of them asked Philip, 'Sir, we would like to talk with Jesus.' Philip went and told Andrew, and the two of them went to Jesus. Jesus talked with the Greeks and answered their enquiries about the Messiah. After they had moved away, Jesus said to Philip and Andrew, 'They were asking about the Messiah and when He will come. They were puzzled about the idea of a suffering Messiah. Yet it is obvious. A grain of wheat is buried in the ground and dies in order that new life will come from it. Similarly, those who follow me and lose their lives will do so only so that new lives of faith will come into being. Anyone who serves me must take that risk, but those who do serve me will be rewarded by my Father in heaven.'

He paused as more people gathered around Him to hear what He had to say. 'Now my heart is troubled. What shall I say? Shall I let this suffering come, or yield to the temptation to escape?' At that moment, there was a distinct sound, like a rumble of thunder. Jesus seemed to be listening for something. 'Did you hear that?' He asked. 'God my Father encourages me to accept the suffering that is coming for that is a necessary part of the plan.' Then Jesus looked up as if He were holding a conversation with someone. 'Father, let Your glory shine through this tragedy.' Then He turned to the crowd again. 'Now is the time for this world to be judged. Now is the time for the Messiah to be killed on behalf of all the people.'

Immediately there were those who said, 'Our Law tells us that the Messiah will live for ever. How, then, can you claim to be the Messiah and yet still talk of death?'

Jesus smiled as He looked at them directly. 'This light will be with you just a little longer. Keep on searching while you have the light with you. Those who walk in spiritual darkness have no idea what they are doing. When you find the truth about life and see the light clearly, then hold on to that light and help others to be the people of the light.'

Jesus stood up and said in a loud voice, 'Whoever believes in me, believes not only in me but in Him who sent me. I have come into the world as a light so that everyone who comes to believe in me will no longer live in darkness. However, whoever does not believe in me and obey me, needs to beware. God, my Father, will judge him. All this is true, not because I speak with my own authority but because I speak in the name of God.'

Jesus, followed by The Twelve, went out of the Temple, out of the city, and once more rested in the Garden of Gethsemane. Jesus found a quiet place and spent some time in prayer. By the time He returned, some of the followers had prepared a light meal and they all ate together. Afterwards, as they prepared for a rest, Jesus said to them, 'Even though the people have seen the healings, heard the teaching and preaching, many of them still do not believe in Me. The prophet Isaiah knew this would happen. He wrote, 'They look, but they do not truly see; they listen, but they do not really hear, and they have met me but they do not recognise me. I came, not to judge the world, but to save it from itself. Those who reject me will meet the true Judge of the world. I came to offer eternal life. That is what I was told to do.' Jesus lay back and the stillness of that place soon eclipsed them all and brought peace and rest.

In the afternoon, Jesus returned to the Temple.

As they were passing the huge horn-shaped offering containers in the Treasury, Judas remarked on their size and wondered how much was given at this time of year. Another of the disciples, Matthew, gave an intelligent guess in reply but then pointed out the difference between the rich people and the poor and their giving. Just at that moment, several merchants came to the Treasury, dropped in their gifts and, as they left, a poor widow came to the same spot and threw in a small coin. 'That will not add much,' said Matthew, disparagingly.

'I'll tell you this for nothing,' said Jesus in a loud voice. 'That poor widow gave more than those merchants. They gave a collection of coins, money that was left over from their bargaining. She gave an offering, a token of her thanks to God, from what little she had. Her's was the greater gift.'

The merchants were quiet as Jesus went on. 'It is not the rich and the powerful who will enter the Kingdom of Heaven, but those who respond to God's invitation, whoever they may be.'

Once again, some Pharisees and members of the King's court arrived in the Temple to try and trap Jesus. Making sure that there were plenty of witnesses, they called to Jesus. 'Teacher, we recognise that you teach the truth as you see it, without worrying about what people will think. You take little account of a person's status and treat everyone the same. Tell us, if you will, is it right that we should pay taxes to Rome?'

Jesus smiled, well aware of the trap that they had set for Him. 'Show me a silver coin,' He said. Someone produced one. Jesus showed it to the crowd. 'Whose face and name is on these coins?' He asked.

'The Emperor's,' several people replied.

'Then give to the Emperor what belongs to the Emperor, but give to God what belongs to God.' There was an amused reaction from the crowd, and a note of approval in their conversation afterwards. The Pharisees said nothing but moved away from Jesus. Jesus sat down ready for a teaching session. 'God has given us sufficient to live on, to keep us alive, but it is the real gifts from God that must be used to His glory.' He paused to give them time to think about what He had said.

'Once upon a time, there was a rich man who decided to go on a foreign holiday. He would be away for a long time so he called together his three senior servants and put them in charge of his property. He brought out of his safe eight thousand silver coins and gave the money to his servants according to their status and ability. He gave one of them five thousand coins, one of them two thousand, and the third one received one thousand. 'I will expect you to give me an accurate account for this money when I return,' he said, and off he went on his holiday.

'The first servant, the one who had received five thousand coins, immediately invested the money and, as a result of his shrewdness, earned another five thousand silver coins. Similarly, the second servant, with the two thousand coins, managed to accrue another two thousand. The third servant, however, was afraid to risk the money committed to his charge. He simply dug a hole in the ground and made sure the money was safe.

'When, after a long time, the owner returned from his holiday, he called in his three servants to go over their accounts. The first servant proudly showed his success and poured out the ten thousand silver coins he now had. "Well done," said the owner, "you have managed well. I will reward your enterprise and give you greater responsibility. Come and share in my homecoming feast." The second servant followed suit, poured out his four thousands coins, and was similarly rewarded. When it was the turn of the third servant, he immediately defended his decision to bury the money. "Sir," he said, "I know that you are a hard man and that you do not tolerate failure. So I played safe, buried the money in a safe place, and here it is just as you gave it to me," and he poured out the one thousand coins onto the table with the other coins.

'The owner was disappointed and annoyed. "You fool!" he said. "I gave you your opportunity, but you failed to take it. Not only did you fail to use the money, but you did not even put it into the bank where at least it would have gained some interest. Being afraid of me is no excuse!" Turning to his other servants, he said, "Take this money and put it with the rest. This servant is dismissed; throw him out!" Jesus paused and looked around the crowd to see what they understood by the story.

Looking directly at the Pharisees on the edge of the crowd, He continued, 'God, my Father, gave you the precious gift of The Law. But you are like that third servant. You have buried it because you are afraid of God. The Law was committed into your care to develop it and help people with their faith, but you have simply applied it as a rigid discipline. All the gifts that God has given must be used to His glory and for the good of His people. Those who use their talents will develop greater abilities for the work of the Kingdom of God. Those who are failures will lose even the small amount of faith that they have.'

Peter asked Jesus, 'Does this story apply to us?'

Jesus replied, 'Peter, the Kingdom of Heaven has been placed into your hands. You must be faithful and wise in your leadership. If you succeed, you will be rewarded with greater responsibility. But beware of the pitfalls for the unfaithful servant.' Then He added, 'Once upon a time, another property owner went away on a holiday and put one of his servants in charge. He was going away for a long time. Because he was away, the servant in charge took advantage of the situation. He relaxed the discipline on the estate and allowed the other servants to eat too much, to drink too much, and generally do what they liked. The owner came back unexpectedly and caught them all in their debauchery. He was furious with them and they were all dismissed.'

'Now society has forgotten the presence of God, and those responsible to God have allowed this licentiousness to proliferate. They will be punished in one way or another. However, you must be like the faithful servant, who, when his master returned unexpectedly, found everything running smoothly on the estate and indeed found that progress was being made.'

Someone, on the edge of the crowd, asked, 'When will this Kingdom of Heaven come into being?'

'Watch and wait,' replied Jesus, and then went on to tell another story. 'Once upon a time there were ten bridesmaids who had been invited to accompany the bridegroom to a wedding. They took their oil lamps with them for the wedding was to take place in the evening. Five of them took an extra supply of oil for no-one knew at what time the wedding would take place. As it turned out, the bridegroom was very late and some of the girls had gone to sleep. It was after midnight before the bridegroom appeared. "Here he comes," shouted the guests. "Come and meet the bridegroom." The ten girls woke up, trimmed their lamps and made themselves ready for the wedding. However, the lamps began to die down because they had been burning for so long. The wise girls, who had brought extra oil with them, managed to refill their lamps, but the foolish ones could not. "Give us some of your oil," the foolish girls asked. "No," the other girls replied, "we need what we have for the wedding. Go to the shops and see if you can buy some." The wise bridesmaids went into the wedding. When the other five girls eventually returned from the shops, they were too late for the wedding was over.

'So,' said Jesus, 'always be ready for you do not know when or how the Kingdom will come. Be on your guard! Don't let yourself become occupied too much with eating and drinking or the anxieties of this life. You may then be too busy or too worried and fail to see the signs of its coming. Be on the alert and pray that you will be ready for that great day.'

'Yes we will,' said the man who asked the question.

'Make sure you do,' replied Jesus, 'for there was once a man who had two sons. To the first one he said, "Son, please go and work in the vineyard today." The young man replied, "No, I don't want to," but later on he changed his mind and went to work. The other son, when asked to work in the vineyard, replied, "Yes sir," but he did not go. Now which one of the two did what his father wanted?'

'The son who went to work,' several people replied.

'Yes,' said Jesus. 'Now there are those whose lives are being changed by coming to know God. They were thieves, prostitutes, and collaborators, saying "No" to God and His ways. But, having found a real faith and begun a personal relationship with God, they have now entered that Kingdom ahead of you. They responded to the preaching of John the Baptist, but you did not. You failed to see that God was at work in him. So be alert for the next time God challenges you.'

Jesus spent the rest of the day teaching and preaching and, when evening came, He and His followers went back to their camp on the Mount of Olives.

CHAPTER 3

TUESDAY

W HENEVER Jesus appeared in the Temple, He was conscious that there were representatives of the religious authorities watching His every move and reporting His every word. It was therefore no great surprise, when He entered the Temple the next day, to see two or three Pharisees and Sadducees on the edge of the crowd. On this occasion He challenged them outright. 'Who do you think the Messiah will be? From which of the Twelve Tribes will He be descended and to whose family tree will He belong?'

'He will be a descendant of David,' they responded with the confidence of someone in authority.

'Yet David called the Messiah "LORD" in one of his Psalms. Now, can something greater come from something lesser? Can humanity create a Messiah?' Once again the Pharisees were silent for they had no answer. Jesus smiled, and there was a murmuring in the crowd. They were amazed at the way He always managed to defeat the authorities.

Jesus sat down to begin His teaching session for the morning. 'The teachers of the Law and the Pharisees are nevertheless authorised to interpret the Law. So you must obey what they say. However, do not copy their actions for they are hypocrites; they do not practise what they preach.

Through their interpretations they make it hard for people to live but make no effort at all to help them. They make sure that everyone sees them and believes them to be holy men, but many are insincere. They wear verses of Scripture on their foreheads and arms, and special tassels on their cloaks as a sign of their deep devotion to God. They love sitting in the best seats at the festivals, the reserved seats in the synagogues, and to be respected and called "Teacher" by everyone around them. Beware of them and their attitudes. Remember everyone matters equally to God. The greatest person must be willing to be the servant of all, for whoever humbles himself will be great.'

Some Sadducees (those who deny that there is a resurrection), standing on the edge of the crowd, delighted with Jesus's attack on the Pharisees, asked Him, 'Teacher, Moses said that if a man who has no children dies then his widow should marry his brother. In this way it is hoped that she will have children and thus perpetuate the family. Now there were seven brothers who used to live here in the city. The eldest married but soon died. Each brother in turn married the widow and died. She was therefore married to all seven! Eventually she too died. In the resurrection, whose wife will she be?'

Jesus shook His head at their pathetic attempt to trap Him into siding with them or to go against their beliefs. He answered, 'In heaven, there is no marriage, nor husbands and wives. So, when the Kingdom of God comes and the dead are raised, there will be no human relationships for everyone will be like the angels. What is important now is that God is the God of the Living. Never mind about the dead!'

This time the Pharisees were the ones to be pleased by His dismissal of the Sadducees' question. They responded by asking another question. 'Teacher, which is the greatest commandment in our Law?'

Jesus answered without any hesitation. 'Love the Lord your God with all your heart, with all your soul and with all your mind. This is the greatest and most important of all the commandments. The second most important commandment is this: Love your neighbour as much as you love yourself. The whole of the Law can be worked out through these two commandments.'

'How does God expect us to love our neighbour in the way that we love Him?' asked someone in the crowd.

Jesus answered, 'Here, in the Temple, there are divisions; between men and women, between Jew and foreigner. With God, the only division is between those who show His love in their lives and those who do not. It is like the herdsman who has to separate the sheep from the goats. To those on His right hand side God will say, "Well done! Come and sit with Me and enjoy the heavenly banquet. You have shown your love for Me for I was hungry and you gave Me food; I was thirsty and you gave Me a drink; I was a stranger and you welcomed Me into your home; I was in need of clothing and you saw to My needs; I was sick and you took care of Me, and I was in prison and you came to visit Me."

'Then those on His right hand side will say, "Lord when did we ever see You hungry or thirsty; a stranger in need of a welcome or in need of clothing; when were You ever ill or in prison and we helped You?" And God will answer by saying, "Because you cared in these ways for the people, My children, it was as if you were caring for Me."

'Then He will turn to those on His left hand side, to those who consider themselves to be good and holy, and He will say, "Get away from Me you selfish people. I was hungry but you gave Me no food; I was thirsty but you offered Me nothing to drink; I was a stranger but you turned your back on Me and ignored My needs; I was in need of clothing but you refused to help; I was ill but you did not care; I was in prison but you did not visit Me." Then these righteous people will declare, "Lord when did we see You hungry and failed to feed You; thirsty and refused You a drink; a stranger and did not welcome You into our homes; in need of clothing and did not help You; ill and in prison and failed to visit You?" Then God will say, "Because you failed to care for those around you, with all their obvious needs, it was as if you failed to help Me."' Those Pharisees still listening to Jesus turned away, understanding full well who He meant and rushed off to report His words to the authorities.

Throughout the morning, Jesus taught the people, answering their questions and amazing them with the clarity of His answers. He spoke as a person of authority, though not one of the religious authorities. Again He and His followers retired to the Gethsemane Garden for rest, and then returned again in the afternoon. This time He went into the Men's Court. There, in front of Him, was a phalanx of Pharisees, as if forming a barrier. As He entered through the gate He stopped and, moved with righteous indignation, addressed the Pharisees.

'You foolish Pharisees! You hypocrites! You lock the doors of the Kingdom of God and prevent people from entering. In doing so you lock yourselves out as well. You travel hundreds of miles, even cross the sea, in order to make one convert. Then, with your indoctrination, you make him twice as bad as yourselves. You are so blind that you cannot see that you are defeating your own purpose. You say that if a man swears on oath, "By the temple of Jerusalem", he is not bound by such a vow. However, if he swears, "By all the gold in the Temple", he is bound by that vow! You idiots! It is because the gold is in the Temple that it becomes holy! Similarly you say if he swears, "By the altar in the Temple", he is not bound by that vow, but if he swears, "By the gifts on the altar", he is bound by that vow. How stupid you are. It is because the gifts are on the altar that they become holy. If you swear, "by all that is in heaven", can't you see that that is a holy vow because God is in heaven and therefore is included?'

'You hypocrites! You are rigid in your observance of the Law with regard to the needs of the people. For example, you give to God one tenth of the harvest of seasoning herbs. But, at the same time, you pay little or no attention to justice, mercy, and honesty. All three are important! You blind guides! You strain your drink to make sure that you do not swallow a fly, and then you accidentally swallow a camel!' This attack brought on an eruption of laughter from those standing behind Him amidst the tension of His devastating criticism.

'You fools! You are meticulous in your cleansing rituals. You clean the outside of the cup and fail to clean the dirt from the inside. You stand there now, pretending to be holy on the outside, but inside you are full of selfish and violent thoughts. Clean the inside first and then the outside will follow. What is inside a man is more important to God. You are like the tombs in the cemetery. The outside looks white and clean but inside they are full of decaying corpses!

'Don't you yet realise what you are doing? You put up wonderful memorials to the great prophet martyrs of the past. You claim that you would never have done such terrible things if you had been alive at that time. But you are doing the same thing, and you will continue to do so. God will send you wise men and prophets. Some you will crucify on trumped up charges; some you will murder, and some you will whip and drive them out of your towns and cities. But you will be to blame. You will be punished! You will be murderers!'

The Pharisees were understandably outraged, and now were determined that Jesus should be silenced. Jesus's followers pulled Him back from the gateway in case there was any violence. None of them spoke to Him for, at that moment, they were afraid of Him and for Him and for themselves, and what the authorities might do to them all. Jesus walked slowly out of the courts of the Temple, back into the noise and hubbub of daily life in the city. Jesus left the Temple and would have liked to have walked along the viaduct going towards the upper city. However, only priests and the nobility were allowed to use that route. Instead He went through the market place. He stopped the disciples and told them that He had to go into the city for a short while. He agreed to meet them just before sunset back at the pool of Five Porches, known as Bethzatha, near the Sheep Gate. The Twelve moved away in another direction. Philip and Nathaniel were talking together when they looked back and saw Judas and a Pharisee in deep conversation.

When, later in the day, Jesus and the Twelve met one another, they made their way back to the Mount of Olives via the Jericho road. As they came to the famous Fig Tree, sure enough, as Jesus had predicted, the old tree was beginning to wither and die. 'When you see the leaves coming on a tree you know that summer is near. So, now, as you see this tree withering and about to die, I tell you the signs are already there for the destruction of Jerusalem. The city and its greatness will pass away but my words will last for ever.'

As they walked along, Judas asked, 'When will all this

take place?'

Jesus was slow to respond, as if thinking of an answer or controlling His emotions at the thought of the destruction of the Holy City. 'No one knows the time or the day when all this will happen. Remember the story of Noah. He spent time building his boat but he did not know when the rain would begin. The people laughed at his predictions, but when the floods did come they were caught unawares and drowned. So be on your guard. Look for the signs. Men will be working in the fields and women at their grinding mills. Suddenly the end will come. Some will be saved and many will not.'

The twelve were in a sombre mood as they climbed the Mount of Olives. When they sat down on the hillside for a rest and looked back on the city in the fading light, they noticed its beauty with the last rays of the sun reflecting off the roof of the Holy of Holies in the Temple. 'It is an awesome sight!' said James.

'Yes,' said Jesus. 'You may well admire the view now. However, the time is coming when not one stone will be left standing on top of another,' and again He was silent for a few minutes as if in mourning. 'Many others will come claiming to be Messiah. Their claims will be false but they will want to lead the people in an attempt to throw off the yoke of Rome. There will be battles, wars, rumours of wars, here and elsewhere. There will be earthquakes and after-shocks, famine and similar disasters. All these will be the signs like the pains warning of the approach of child birth.' He paused. 'After my death there will be persecution. The authorities will want to arrest you and all those who follow me. Many will give up their faith. Some will betray others of our number in order to save themselves. There will be such scenes of evil that people will lose their faith and their belief in a God of love. But whoever holds onto his faith and remains firm and true to the Kingdom will be truly rewarded.'

'Rome's patience with the Jews will finally snap and they will turn our Temple into a Roman temple dedicated to the worship of Jove. The Holy of Holies will house statues of Roman gods, and men will bow down to them and no longer to the God of our Fathers. That will be the time, the time to run away. Those working in the fields must not take time to go back to their houses to collect belongings. It will be awful for pregnant women and women with babies. They must get away as fast as they can and when they can. These foreign vultures will hover and swoop down on anyone who is left and, in one sense, devour them. There will be an eclipse of the moon, and people will be afraid that this will be the end of the world. But it is not.' In the city, the sound of a trumpet could be heard marking the end of one day and the beginning of another. 'Another trumpet will sound in those days. For God will come in all His glory to set up His Kingdom on earth.'

Jesus stopped talking and there was silence. All they could hear was the noise of people in their camp sites preparing for the night. They all got up and made their way back to their site.

CHAPTER 4

WEDNESDAY

THE following day was like an oasis between the Wilderness of Conflict and the Desert of Disaster. Jesus did not go into the city to the Temple but spent the day with His friends in the village of Bethany. Simon, a prosperous man but struck down with leprosy, had been one of those healed by Jesus. Naturally Jesus was always welcome in His home. As He was in the locality, Simon had sent Jesus an invitation. Jesus, and the Twelve, duly arrived and enjoyed the peace and quiet of the place as well as the hospitality. However, in the evening, the time for the main meal, a very different challenge to Jesus came from His own disciples.

Such a meal, with such a distinguished guest, as usual became a public occasion. The meal was held in the courtyard round the spring of water bubbling up through the ground. People gathered in the courtyard, but back from the guests, in order to hear the speaker after the meal was completed. During the meal, Mary, the sister of Lazarus, and therefore a neighbour, was standing on the edge of the crowd because only the men were allowed to eat at this meal. She came towards Jesus who was sitting on a brightly coloured cushion. She stood by Him, took a phial of ointment from a chain that was round her neck, poured out the ointment over Jesus's head and then smashed the phial to pieces on the ground. While she was doing this, Jesus remained where He was, His head bowed as if in prayer. When she had finished, the woman returned to the crowd.

Matthew, Judas, and others of the disciples, were amazed at what had happened, and angry with Jesus for letting it happen. 'What a terrible waste!' exclaimed Matthew to Alphaeus, 'there was a year's wages in that phial. It is meant to be used a drop at a time!'

Judas added, 'That could have been accepted as a gift and sold to feed a thousand people or given to help the poor. What on earth was He thinking about?'

Jesus knew what they were saying without having to hear their words. He gazed at them all and suddenly there was silence. 'Why are you so bothered about what this woman has done? Yes, of course, it could have been sold for money and given to the poor. But that would not solve their problem. This woman was moved to anoint me with what is her ointment. It is a prophetic act prompted by God My Father. This anointing says, by this outward sign, that I am accepted as a priest, prophet, and a king, like those who are anointed at the induction to their office. She has also warned you that I will soon die for she has anointed me ready for my burial. She has shown you the true cost of love. By smashing the phial she has marked me as someone special, someone holy, for such a phial must never be used for anyone else.' Jesus paused as if anticipating some response from the Twelve. He went on, 'When my story is told, this woman, and her act of love, will be remembered also.'

After the meal was over, Jesus preached to the crowd which had gathered in the courtyard. Seemingly unnoticed, Judas crept away, incensed by what had happened, upset because he thought Jesus had humiliated him in front of everyone else, including His fellow disciples, and disillusioned with the lack of aggression by Jesus towards the Roman authorities. He sought out the Pharisee who had approached Him on the previous day and entered into negotiations to betray Jesus.

CHAPTER 5

THURSDAY

ANY Festival at Jerusalem brings with it its own excitement, but the Festival of Unleavened Bread and the Passover has the added experience of a packed city bursting at the seams. As Jesus and some of the Twelve entered the city you could feel the excitement. Most people were involved, one way or another, in the preparation for the Festivals. In camp, in the morning, Peter and the disciples had come to Jesus to ask what arrangements had been made for their celebrations, and what they could do to help.

'I want two of you to go into the city,' Jesus had responded. 'When you go in through the Sheep Gate, you will soon see a man carrying a pitcher of water on his shoulder. Follow him and when he enters a house, go with him and find the owner. Say to that man, "The Master asks where is the room that He has booked for the Passover meal?" He will show you a large furnished upstairs room. That is the place where we will celebrate the Passover. Please make all the necessary preparations.' Sure enough, everything happened exactly as Jesus said, and had planned. The two disciples and the house servants prepared everything for the meal with their usual meticulous care.

Jesus walked casually through the city, talking with anyone who stopped to talk with Him. However, most people were in a hurry, struggling to cope with the crowds as they made their way from place to place. As the day wore on His thoughts turned to the evening meal. The noise from the animals being slaughtered and the smell of blood pervaded the city. He had arranged for the Twelve to meet at the Gate of the Essenes, and from there He would guide them to the upper room. Judas had soon disappeared, but Jesus knew that he would reappear in time for the meal. Judas, led on by personal hurt, had succumbed to temptation. The authorities had offered him thirty pieces of silver to betray Jesus. His job was to find the right time and opportunity for Jesus to be arrested without there being crowds of people about. Judas was expected to send a message to the authorities giving them the time and the place where this could happen, and they would do the rest.

At the right time in the evening, Jesus met the disciples and they strolled to the upper room. The disciples stood talking to Peter and Andrew as the latter described what they had had to do in order to prepare for the evening meal. While they were talking, Jesus folded up His sleeves, tucked His outer garment under His belt, picked up a bowl of water, a washing cloth and a towel and came towards the nearest disciple. He knelt in front of him, took off his sandals and started to wash his feet. There was a stunned silence. Because there was always a reason why Jesus did things, most of the disciples just allowed it to take place. Peter, however, was embarrassed. When Jesus came to him and knelt in front of him he burst out, asking, 'Are you really going to wash my feet, Lord?'

'You will not understand just now what I am doing but one day you will,' Jesus answered.

Peter moved backwards. 'You will never wash my feet. That's the job of a servant!' he exclaimed.

Jesus looked full into Peter's eyes. 'If I do not wash your feet, Peter,' He said, 'you cannot be my disciple.'

Peter, impetuous as ever, immediately dropped to his knees and replied, 'then, Lord, do not wash only my feet but wash my hands and my head as well!'

Jesus smiled at him for He was amused at Peter's reaction. 'If you have had a bath, you do not need to wash again, except for your feet.' So Jesus continued His task until He had washed the feet of each disciple. Then He washed His hands, undid His gathered clothes and sat down on the cushion at the head of the feast. The disciples followed His example and sat on the cushions at places strategically arranged around the long flat table. John sat on one side of Jesus, and Peter on the other. On the table in front of Jesus were two loaves, a jug of wine and a cup, ready for the ceremony known as the Seder.

Before saying the Grace, Jesus said to them, 'Do you realise what I have just done? You call me Rabbi, Teacher, Lord, and so I am. But if I, your Rabbi, Teacher, Lord have performed this humble task for you, surely you should be ready to do it for one another? I have set you the example because I want you to understand that no Lord is greater than his servant; no Master is greater than his slave, and the prophet is not greater than the one who gave him the message to preach. Everyone matters equally to God. So be humble and be willing to do the work of a slave or servant if this is what your heavenly Father wishes.'

Then Jesus led the ceremony of the Seder by saying the Kiddush, a prayer for the sanctifying of the evening, all that would take place and everything that would be consumed. He covered His head, lifted the bread in His two hands, asked God's blessing upon it and all the food that would be eaten. Then He broke it, gave a piece to John, and then in turn the disciples passed the bread to each other, first of all breaking a piece off before passing it to the one on their right hand side. As they were doing this, Jesus said, 'This bread is my body, soon to be broken for humanity. Take and eat, all of you, and as you do so, remember that I am offering myself to you.' There was now a sadness that was added to the solemnity of the occasion. Then Jesus poured the wine into the cup, lifted it and asked a blessing on that cup and all the wine that would be drunk that night in the Passover meal. Then He passed the cup to John and invited him to drink from it. Once more, each, in turn, offered the cup to their neighbour, and drank from it. As they were doing this, Jesus said, 'This is my blood, soon to be poured out for you and for humanity. This is a token of my love for you and the seal on God's Covenant promise of a personal relationship with Him. When you break bread and drink wine together in future, remember this occasion and remember me. This is the last time that I shall eat and drink in this way with you.'

There was a stunned silence, a dread of what was to come, a fear of what was going to happen after this Passover meal.

'Why do you say these things?' asked Peter, voicing the question in the mind of them all. 'We will never let you down. We will never let anything bad happen to you! I would rather die first!' he exclaimed.

Jesus shook His head slowly. 'One of you has already betrayed me to the authorities, and this very night you will all run away and leave me,' He said. Peter was just about to say something else when Jesus continued, 'And you, Peter, will deny even knowing me, before the cock crows and the sun comes up.' Peter sat back, shocked, but still shaking his head in denial.

At this there was a general outcry and words like 'Never' and 'No' and 'Not me, Lord', were heard from all of them.

Jesus then indicated for them to be silent, and He also called for the servants to come and clear away the Seder and serve the Passover meal. It took some time to bring everything in - and lay it all on the low table in the right places and with the correct ritual. This was a full meal with everything from lamb to wine, and including unleavened bread and salt water, bitter herbs, and the Charosheth paste. When all was at last ready, Jesus stood up to pray. He gave the formal prayer of the Seder, thanking God for this memorial of freeing the People of God and once more leading them to a new life. Then He washed His hands, the first of three such occasions during the meal. He stretched forward, took a piece of parsley and a piece of lettuce, dipped them in the salt water, and ate them. The Passover Meal had begun.

The meal followed the traditional pattern with the telling of the old story, and the full eating ritual reminding them all of the time of suffering in Egypt. When it came to the time of eating the Sop, Jesus leant forward, took two pieces of Passover bread, placed some of the bitter herbs between them and then scooped up some Charosheth paste with this sandwich. The paste, made of apples, dates, pomegranates, and nuts also had sticks of cinnamon through it. Here was the reminder of the materials used to make bricks in the time of slavery. As Jesus withdrew His hand, He touched the hand of Judas who was doing the same thing. Jesus looked into the eyes of Judas and saw fear, fear of being found out. Jesus looked away but now both knew the truth. Judas was the one who would betray Him.

After this, the main time of eating began. They had eaten nothing since mid-day, and the shank of lamb, as well as the rest of the food, had to be eaten. There was time for conversation. Nathaniel, with a certain amount of emotion, asked Jesus, 'Lord, earlier this evening you told us that you were leaving us and gave the impression that you were going to die. What did you really mean?'

Jesus replied, 'Do not be worried or upset. Death is not so terrible. You believe in God and heaven, so believe in me and my words. Heaven is like a guest house, a home, and there are very many rooms. It is as if I were going there to prepare a room for you. When all is ready, I will come back for you and escort you to your heavenly home. I have taught you about the Kingdom so you know the road to heaven that I shall take tomorrow.'

Thomas, still puzzled, asked Him, 'We do not know where you are going tomorrow, so how can we know what road to take?'

'Thomas,' said Jesus with great patience, 'I am the road, the right path, the truth about life. No-one comes to know God without coming to know me first of all. Because you have come to know me and believe in me, so you have come to know God and believe in Him.'

Philip interrupted, 'Lord, show us your Father, show us God, that is all we need to know.'

'Oh Philip, after all this time, don't you yet know who I am?' He paused. 'Whoever has seen me has seen my Father also. He and I are one. I am in the Father and the Father is in me. You cannot divide God into two. I am telling you the truth, but I know that it is difficult to understand. Those who believe in me and accept me, and have become my disciples, will be able to be in ministry for me. You will be able to do all that I have done, and even greater things. If you love me, as you say you do, then you will obey my commands. If you ask anything in my name, I will see that it is done. In a little while you will see me no more, but my spirit will be with you. He will be like a Comforter, giving you the strength, the inspiration, and the courage that you need.'

Judas asked Him, 'Lord, why have you now shown your real self to us but not to the world outside? Think what you could achieve for the people of Israel with your power, freedom from Roman rule, a real peace.'

'It is my peace that I give to you. This is not a peace that the world understands, a peace that is merely the absence of war. My peace is built on a relationship with God, a peace of mind,' Jesus replied. 'This peace of mind is a peace which comes when communities, peoples, and nations learn to live in harmony with one another.' Judas, obviously frustrated, got up from his seat. Jesus, still looking at him, made His last appeal to him, though it sounded like a challenge. 'Go and do what you must do.' After a moment's hesitation, Judas left the room. The other disciples assumed that he was going to see the owner of the house in order to pay the bills for the evening.

At the drinking of the third cup of wine, the Cup of Thanksgiving, Jesus prayed the set prayer; 'Blessed art Thou, O Lord our God, King of the universe, who has created the fruit of the vine.'

The disciples replied, 'Amen!'

Jesus once more addressed them. 'I am the real vine, and my Father is the vine grower. Every branch that does not bear fruit is cut off and, at the right time, every branch that has born fruit is pruned back in order to produce more fruit. A branch cannot bear fruit on its own. It is part of the whole vine and is dependent upon it. You, who have already born fruit, will be like those branches that have been pruned. Remain attached to me for you cannot bear fruit without me.' He paused and looked sadly at the door through which Judas had left.

'I am the vine,' He went on, 'and you are the branches. Together we will produce much fruit. Remember my words, obey my commands, go on loving me, just as I have obeyed my Father and thus have remained in His love. I have told you all this now so that your understanding may be complete. The most important command I have given you is to love one another.

'The greatest example of that love is when one person gives his life for another. So I go to offer my life for you out of my love for you. I chose you and appointed you to be my disciples. Go now and produce fruit, fruit that will endure for ever. If the world hates you, remember it hated me first. If they persecute you, remember that they persecuted me first. But do not despair for I have overcome the world!'

Jesus then filled the cup for the fourth and final time with wine, and together they sang the Great Hallel. 'Oh give thanks to the Lord for He is good, for His steadfast love endures for ever!' After the Passover meal was completed, they sang a hymn and then they all made their way to the Garden of Gethsemane for it was late in the night. Judas joined the Twelve once more outside the house.

John Mark, a young man and the son of the house owner where this Passover meal had taken place, had met Jesus on the occasions when Jesus had visited His father and mother.

On this particular night, having talked to Jesus and the Twelve when they arrived, he had shared the Passover meal with his own family. He had eventually gone to his bed. As he stood at the window, he noticed a man hiding in the shadows. To his surprise, he then saw one of the Twelve come out of the house, pause, and then go over to the man in the shadows. They talked for a few moments, and then the man in the shadows went away.

Later that night, John Mark was woken by the noise of marching feet. When he looked out of the window, he saw a phalanx of the Temple Police, fully armed, marching past the house. Suddenly he realised what was happening. Someone had set a trap for Jesus, and now the Temple Police were going to arrest Him. John Mark, still in his night clothes, went downstairs, out of the house and ran for all he was worth by a different route in order to get to the Garden of Gethsemane before the police so that he could warn Jesus.

By the time Jesus and the Twelve had reached the garden, they were all tired. Jesus asked some of the Twelve to remain where they were while Peter, James, and John accompanied Him to another part of the garden. When He reached a place apart from the rest, He told the three disciples to rest there while He went on a little further. 'Stay here, but keep awake until I return.' When He had moved on, Jesus stopped, knelt for prayer and said, 'Father, the hour has come. Give me the strength that I need to go through this particular ordeal and to complete the work that I was sent to do. I have offered them eternal life, a relationship with You now and for ever. I have given You the glory. I have preached the message that You gave me, and now they know that all I have taught and preached comes from You.'

'I pray for them. Soon I will return to You but they will be left to face the world. Father, keep them safe through Your almighty power. I have kept them safe while I have been with them, and not one of them has been lost, well, just the one who has betrayed me. But I pray for him too.

'Yet I pray not only for them but for all those who will believe in me even though they have never met me. I pray that they will find strength in their unity, in their togetherness, just as You and I are one. I pray for this success so that through their united witness, others will realise who I am and that You sent me. I pray that the love that You have for me will also be in them.'

Jesus got up from where He had been praying, and returned to Peter and the other two. He found them sound asleep, for they were so tired after their meal. He smiled a wry smile. 'Couldn't you stay awake just for one hour more? The spirit was willing but the flesh is weak.' So He returned to His private place and prayed once more.

As He thought of the immediate future, He began to perspire heavily. For a few moments His body began to shake uncontrollably. Then, when He had regained control, He prayed, 'Father, I know what lies ahead, I have seen it too often. If this cup of suffering is unnecessary, then let it pass me by. However, if it is necessary, then let Your will be done.'

CHAPTER 6

FRIDAY

SUDDENLY the peace of the night and of the garden was shattered with the noise of a young man shouting, and then the sound of tramping feet. Jesus got up and hurried back to Peter, James, and John, and woke them immediately. 'Come on! Wake up! The time is now! I am about to be put into the hands of the authorities.' Jesus had reached the point of no return. He was still speaking when the Temple police arrived. They were heavily armed. All the disciples were now wide awake.

'What is happening?' they asked, for they were bewildered. The Temple Police stopped when they reached the Twelve as if waiting for some order.

'What shall we do?' asked Judas, and rushed forward to Jesus, held Him by the arms, and kissed Him on the cheek. This seemed to be a sign, for immediately the Police arrested Jesus.

'Do you dare to betray me with a kiss?' Jesus asked Judas. Then He turned to the officer in charge. 'Did you have to come at night, fully armed, as if I were a terrorist? I have been in the Temple much of the week in broad daylight. Couldn't you have arrested me then?'

The officer said nothing in reply, but barked out the orders.

'Bind Him and bring Him along.' He turned to the disciples. 'You had better bring them as well.' The disciples, already afraid and confused, panicked. They suddenly ran in all directions through the gardens. John Mark ran as well, and his night clothes caught on a bush and were torn off, so he ran away naked. The officer looked at Jesus, amused and with pity. 'My men would never desert me,' he boasted.

Jesus did not resist arrest and, though He was treated roughly by the police, His lack of aggression made the whole event easy for them. Jesus was first taken to the house of Annas. He was the real power behind the position of High Priest, having been High Priest himself and having made sure that his family dominated that position. He owned the money-changing stalls in the Temple, so here was his moment for revenge. He gloated as Jesus was brought before him. However, he had no authority to sit in judgement on Jesus, so that, having satisfied himself with taunting Jesus, he sent Him on to his son-in-law Caiaphas, who was High Priest, and to his house in the Upper City.

Caiaphas was concerned to be fair and to be seen to be fair. So he questioned Jesus about His teaching and about the status of the Twelve. Jesus replied, 'I have always spoken publicly to everyone; this last week all my teaching has been in the Temple courts quite openly. I have never said anything in secret. Question those who listened to me. They will answer your question.' One of the guards standing by Jesus struck Him across the mouth.

'How dare you talk to the High Priest in that way!' he exclaimed. 'Show some respect for him!'

Jesus ignored this outburst. He looked straight at Caiaphas and challenged him. 'If I have said anything that is wrong, then tell everyone here what it was. But if what I have taught is right, then why I should I be treated in this way?'

'Take Him away,' commanded Caiaphas, irritated by the attitude of Jesus. After Jesus had left, he remained in his seat thinking. After some time he said to his advisers, 'It is better that one man should die rather than take the risk of a riot, and then many people would be killed. Our Roman masters will not tolerate even the hint of revolt. Call a meeting of the Sanhedrin and we will prepare the charge against this Jesus. Then we will send Him to the Governor.'

While all this was taking place, Peter, who, with his head covered to avoid recognition, had followed the police at a distance, was outside the house. He had waited outside the home of Annas, and now followed the procession on to the house of the High Priest. In the courtyard, the police escort stood round a brazier warming themselves. There were some young women, servants, who had brought out some wine for them. There were several other people in the courtyard taking advantage of the warmth. Peter, being very cautious, bided his time. As the night went on, he became cold and so drew nearer to the fire in order to get warm. One of the girls, serving the wine, came to Peter and looked at him intently. 'I know you,' she said. 'You're one of those followers of Jesus. I saw you by Him in the procession a few days ago!' she exclaimed.

'No,' said Peter, turning away from her and from the light of the fire. 'You must be mistaken. I am not one of His disciples.' Some time later, exactly the same thing happened again. Once more Peter told her that she was mistaken and that he was not one of the man's followers.

Members of the Sanhedrin were now gathering. Normally

they would meet in the Hall of Hewn Stone in the Temple precincts. However, this meeting was different. There had to be at least twenty-three members present of the seventy who were entitled to sit in the Council. When they were ready, Jesus was brought in before the Council. One by one, witnesses were brought in who denounced Jesus for what they claimed He had said and done. Caiaphas became frustrated. The witnesses either reported trivial matters that were useless when trying to find a capital charge, or they contradicted each other when there was something worthwhile. Eventually, two witnesses did get their story right. 'He claimed,' they said 'that He was able to pull down God's Temple and build it up again in three days!' Caiaphas was puzzling over what charge he could bring against Jesus with this evidence.

'What answer do you have to that accusation?' challenged Caiaphas. Jesus remained standing and said nothing.

Caiaphas stood up and shouted at Jesus, more out of frustration than anything else. 'In the name of the living God, I put you under oath. Are you the Messiah? Is it true that you claim to be the Son of God?' Members of the Sanhedrin held their breath. Caiaphas had overplayed his hand for though this was the only charge that could warrant the death penalty, if Jesus denied it there was nothing that they could do. They waited, watching Jesus carefully. 'Well?' demanded Caiaphas. 'I am waiting for your answer!'

Jesus looked straight at Caiaphas once more. 'It is as you say. And I will tell you this, on Judgement Day you will see me in Heaven sitting at the right hand of God the Father.'

It was a moment of triumph and drama. Caiaphas shouted, 'Blasphemy!' the one charge that he needed. As a symbolic act, he took off his cloak and tore it in half and threw in on t h e floor in front of everyone. He turned to the members of the Sanhedrin. 'We have no need of further witnesses for you yourselves have become witnesses. The charge is blasphemy. What do you say?'

From all over the room came the reply, 'Blasphemy! Blasphemy!' There was a mixture of relief and triumph.

'Take Him to the Governor,' ordered Caiaphas with great satisfaction.

The shouting was heard in the courtyard, and everyone stopped what they were doing, conscious that something important was happening. An officer shouted an order and the police tidied themselves, picked up their weapons and formed a guard by the door of the house. The people in the courtyard, including Peter, drew near to the door, eager to see what was happening. As Jesus was being brought out, some of them started jeering and shouting, but not Peter. The same servant girl noticed Peter's reluctance. 'I know that you are one of His followers,' she challenged.

'No, I am not,' Peter replied forcibly, 'I never met the man.' At that very moment, Peter looked towards the door and there was Jesus looking straight at him. A cock crowed nearby, and Peter noticed that the first light of dawn could be seen above the roof of the courtyard. He left the courtyard after the police guard and their followers had left. He found his way back to the Garden of Gethsemane, to the place where he had gone to sleep, sank to his knees and wept long and bitterly.

As if to make the point that Jesus was a dangerous criminal, the Temple police had now put Jesus in chains. With His escort

He was taken from the house of Caiaphas, the short distance to the Praetorium. This was the new name for what had been Herod's Royal Palace before the occupation and was built with three famous towers, Hippicus, Phassel, and Mariamne. The Roman guard heard the procession some way off, and were ready and at attention by the time the party arrived. At the palace gate, the prisoner's escort was stopped.

'What is all this?' asked the officer on duty.

'Prisoner for sentencing,' was the curt reply from the representative of the High Priest.

'But the Governor is in bed,' continued the officer.

'I am not surprised, but this is urgent and serious business. This man needs to be sentenced and executed before the day is out, for the Sabbath begins this evening,' the representative continued, and he handed him the warrant and accusation written by Caiaphas.

'Wait here,' ordered the officer, and he went inside to make enquiries. Some time later, a more senior officer emerged, asked the same questions and got the same answer.

'Why is it so urgent, other than this business about the Sabbath?' he asked.

'The offence demands the death penalty. We are not allowed to pass such a sentence while we are under Roman occupation.' Then, clutching at a straw of hope, he said, 'This man claims to be a King. We are afraid that there might be a riot in the city, even an uprising. We want to avoid this, and we are sure the Governor would as well.' This last sentence had the desired effect.

'All right, hand the prisoner over to us, and I will personally see the Governor. I will send a messenger to the High Priest when the Governor has passed sentence.' The High Priest's representative thanked the officer, and with a smirk of cunning and satisfaction on his face, marched, with the Temple police, back to the High Priest to report what had happened.

Jesus, now very tired through lack of sleep, and worn out through walking through the city in chains, was dragged into the palace courtyard. There He was left to stand in the cold of the morning. Some soldiers, who had heard what had happened, were curious to see a Jewish King. When they saw this tired and bedraggled figure, they started to laugh and taunt Jesus. 'Good morning, your majesty,' said one, and saluted Jesus. Another took off his outer scarlet coat and laid it over the shoulders of Jesus. 'You forgot your royal robe, your majesty,' he said. Two others tore off some twigs from the thorn bush growing in the courtyard, twisted them together to make a circle, and then placed it on Jesus's head. 'Your crown, your majesty,' they mocked, and others now had come and were laughing at the spectacle, and called out 'Long live the King of the Jews!' 'Isn't this the miracle worker?' asked another. At that, one or two soldiers came round the back of Jesus and slapped Him across the head. 'Now then, miracle worker, tell us, which one of us hit you?' Finally, one soldier approached Jesus. 'Come on, stand upright, look like a king,' and he tried to force Jesus into standing to attention. Jesus was too weak. By now His hair was matted with perspiration and the congealed blood from where the thorns had broken the skin. 'You, a king? You're pathetic!' and he spat into Jesus's face. Everyone laughed. 'Attention,' shouted a junior officer as he heard a senior officer coming into the courtyard. The soldiers came to attention. 'Bring the prisoner in,' ordered the senior officer. Jesus was immediately surrounded by four soldiers acting as prisoner's escort, His newly acquired royal robes were removed, and He was taken inside the palace.

In a small ante-chamber of the palace, two guards stood either side of a chair. Jesus was made to stop and stand while they all waited for Pilate, the Roman governor, to appear. They came smartly to attention as the Governor entered. 'What is all this nonsense? What is so important that I am forced to get out of my bed? This had better be worthwhile!' said Pilate, and he sat down in the chair. An officer handed the charge sheet from the High Priest over to Pilate. Pilate read it moodily. 'Blasphemy?' he asked suddenly. 'What has that got to do with me?' and he was obviously irritated by the whole experience. 'What have you to say for yourself?' he said, challenging Jesus.

Jesus said nothing. He just stood there.

'Where does He come from?' demanded Pilate.

'From Galilee,' replied the officer, pointing to some detail on the warrant.

'Then take Him to Herod. Let the Fox get out of bed and deal with the matter,' he ordered, and smiled at the prospect of Herod being dragged out of bed for such a trivial matter. He left the room.

Herod's palace, the Palace of the Hasmonaeans, could easily be seen from the towers of the Praetorium. Once more, Jesus was escorted through the city, this time with Roman soldiers who banged on the door of the palace when they arrived. After explanations and delays, Jesus was eventually summoned to come in front of Herod who was sitting on his makeshift throne and looking somewhat dishevelled, having dressed hurriedly. He was amused, and there was a hint of gloating in his eyes as he saw the pathetic figure of Jesus standing before him. 'Well, well, well,' he said. 'The miracle worker stands before me at last,' and he took a drink from a goblet in his hand. 'Come on then,' he taunted, 'show me your miraculous powers. Perform a miracle for me!' he commanded. Jesus stood there silently. Several times he tried to goad Jesus into action but he got no response.

'Send for the High Priest,' he shouted irritably, and he left the room.

Some time later, representatives from the Sanhedrin arrived. Herod returned and asked for their report. They told him what had happened, and continued by making strong accusations against Jesus. Herod held up his hand for them to be quiet. 'You do not have to convince me,' he said, obviously sympathetic to the idea of getting rid of Jesus. 'It is the Governor that you have to convince. Pilate is not going to do anything with the blasphemy charge.'

'He also claimed to be a King,' said one of the representatives. Herod's expression changed. 'King of the Jews,' continued the man, sensing his opportunity. Now the Herod dynasty had a reputation for violence when it came to protecting the throne.

'Then make that the charge,' Herod demanded, and walked determinedly out of the room. Writing materials were sent for, and the new charge added to the warrant. So Jesus was once more escorted through the city streets, this time with an escort of Herod's personal guard and leaders of the Jewish authorities. By now, word had got out about Jesus and His arrest, and there were a number of people who were curious to know what was happening.

When Pilate had gone back to his bedroom, his wife asked what had happened. Pilate told her about Jesus. There was a sharp intake of breath. 'What's the matter?' Pilate asked his wife.

'I dreamt about Him last night,' she replied. 'Pilate,' she pleaded, 'have nothing to do with this man.'

'Don't worry,' he replied, 'I've sent Him over to Herod to deal with Him.' So he was a little apprehensive when later he heard that Herod had sent Jesus back to him for judgement. He also was intrigued to hear that the charge had been adjusted to include claiming to be a King and causing political unrest. He ordered that Jesus be brought to him. This time he took more time looking at Jesus. No man could look less regal. 'Are you a king?' he asked Jesus.

Jesus, for the first time, looked up at Pilate. 'Are you personally asking me this question,' challenged Jesus, 'or is this a ploy for me to condemn myself?'

Pilate looked at Jesus, suddenly aware that this was no terrorist, no revolutionary, standing in front of him. A man like Pilate must have had some previous experience with terrorism before being sent to such a volatile situation as Jerusalem. 'I want to know,' he said plainly, emphasising the word 'I'.

Jesus responded. 'They do not understand,' He said patiently. 'My kingdom is not a political kingdom, but a spiritual one. It is made up of citizens who love the Lord God and will obey Him alone.' And so, for a limited period of time, Pilate asked Jesus questions, but it was more like an interview than an interrogation. Finally, Jesus said, 'I am the way for these people to find God. I am the one to show them the truth about God.'

Pilate then asked a rhetorical question, 'Yes, but what is truth?' For a moment there was silence. Both Pilate and Jesus were by now conscious of the noise of a large crowd outside in the courtyard. An officer came into the room and spoke urgently to Pilate. Pilate got up, looked at Jesus, and then left the officer guarding Jesus while he went outside and into the courtyard. There, to his surprise, he found the courtyard packed with people, and he sensed an aggressive atmosphere in the way that they shouted when he appeared. This was no crowd. It was already a mob, and even the soldiers were anxious. Standing on the top step and looking down on the people, he held up his hand for silence. 'What do you want?' he challenged, when they were quiet.

'We want justice,' the crowd shouted back, and Pilate was aware that this was, in fact, an organised situation.

'I have examined Jesus, and I find no fault with Him,' he said. 'If the charge is blasphemy, then that is nothing to do with me. Take Him and punish Him yourselves.' He was about to turn his back on them when someone shouted.

'He claims that He is a King. That is subversion. You are no friend of Caesar's if you let such an accusation pass.' By now the matter was becoming serious, for such a challenge would not go unreported to Rome.

He tried a different tack. 'Look,' he said. 'At every Passover Festival, I release one prisoner as a gesture of good will.' He stopped, gave an order to an officer behind him. In a few moments, Jesus was brought out to the courtyard. 'Behold, the man to be released!' he shouted.

The crowd erupted into a cacophony of shouts. There was booing and jeering, and things were getting ugly.

'Who do you want me to release then?' he asked.

After a few moments, a voice from the crowd shouted,

'Barrabas. Release Barrabas.' The crowd took up the cry and shouted for Barrabas to be released. He was a notorious criminal, imprisoned for murder and causing a riot.

'And what shall I do with Jesus?' Pilate asked the crowd.

'Crucify Him,' some shouted, and again the excited crowd took up the shout. 'Crucify Him, crucify Him, crucify Him!'

'Crucify Him yourselves,' he shouted back in disgust. 'He is your King,' he shouted defiantly.

'Kill Him, Crucify Him!' the crowd shouted, and now the soldiers were getting unnerved and they held their weapons at the ready.

Pilate was still not ready to give in to their demands. 'Shall I crucify your King?'

One lone voice shouted back, 'We have no King but Caesar!' The crowd took up the shout and in seconds it had become a chant. Pilate was beaten, and he knew it. He turned to an officer and gave another order. The crowd gradually went quiet as they waited to see what was about to happen.

Two servants carried in Pilate's special chair and placed it in the area on top of the courtyard steps known as the Stone Pavement. This indicated that Pilate as Governor was about to make an important judgement. The crowd watched as the two servants then brought out a bowl of water and a towel. Pilate sat down in the chair, and, with elaborate and obvious gestures, washed his hands in front of them. 'I am not responsible for this man's death,' he shouted defiantly to them. 'This is your doing entirely. His blood is on your hands!' The crowd cheered and shouted yet again. Pilate got up from his chair, looked sadly at Jesus and made his way back into the palace.

Jesus was then taken by an officer with an escort to the fortress of Antonia and put into the cells there. The grating, acting as a sort of roof, was lifted and Jesus was lowered into a stone wall cell where there were two other prisoners under sentence of death.

Orders were given, preparations made by the carpenters, and eventually three crosses were laid out in the back courtyard of the palace ready for use. A centurion and escort were ordered to carry out the crucifixions and a further escort of soldiers was ordered to act as guards just in case of trouble.

Later, when everything and everyone was ready, the prisoners were hauled out of the cell and brought into the courtyard. Each in turn was tied to the whipping post and beaten, for this was one way of making sure that they died quickly on the cross, and then the soldiers would not have to hang around waiting too long.

When it was the turn of Jesus to be whipped, He was dragged forward to the post and His hands were tied to the iron rings on either side at the top of the post. His outer garment was removed from His shoulders, but not torn off. The whip, with iron pellets in the end of each thin leather strip, tore into a man's flesh with ease. Jesus felt the pain from the first lash.

When He was a young man in the workshop at home, Joseph had taught Him how to cope with pain. 'Think of something else and concentrate on it, then you will be able to bear pain.' Jesus now held tight to the rings and recalled some of the scriptures He knew, and repeated them to himself. He remembered the words of the Psalmist, 'We fall crushed to the ground; we lie defeated in the dust. Come to our aid! Because of Your constant love, save us!' For a time it helped, and then He lost consciousness and the whipping ceased. A soldier threw a bucket of water over Him and then untied His hands from the rings.

In spite of the early hour, a noisy crowd was waiting for the doors of this courtyard to open, and for the crucifixion procession to begin. The prisoners would be taken along the passages near the outer wall of the city until they reached the busy city gates not far from the hill known as The Skull where all the executions took place.

Inside the courtyard, the main centre plank for each cross was laid over the right shoulder of each prisoner. Each one held the beam with their right hand and virtually dragged the beam along the ground for the beams were so heavy. In front of each prisoner, a soldier carried a board, marked with gypsum, giving the offence. This was meant to act as a deterrent. These soldiers now took their places. When everything was ready, the centurion gave the order and the gates were opened. There was a roar from the crowd. The guard, weapons at the ready, made a way through the crowd for the procession to follow. Jesus was the last to leave the courtyard, and the jeering increased from some.

It was a long road to the place of crucifixion, and the narrow street was packed. At one point, when the procession stopped because of the crowds, a woman came forward and wiped the face of Jesus with a cloth. All three men faltered at some point, but no-one fell until they came to the city gate. Here there were greater problems because of the people trying to get in, and the crowd trying to get out. It was at this point, where the procession had stopped, that Jesus no longer had the strength to carry the beam and He fell down onto His knees. The nearest soldier shouted at Him, even kicked Him, but the centurion, coming to see what was the matter, saw at once that Jesus would not be able to carry the cross piece any further. Looking around at the crowd, he saw a tall strong young man trying to get in through the city gate.

'Hey you,' he shouted at the man, 'what's your name?'

'Me, sir?' the man replied, bewildered by such a sudden demand.

'Yes you,' shouted the centurion.

'Simon, sir,' the man replied.

'And where are you from?' the centurion continued.

'From Cyrene, sir,' he replied again.

'Right, Simon from Cyrene, come and carry this beam,' and he pointed to the one placed on the shoulder of Jesus. Everyone knew that a Roman soldier had the right to make such a demand, and to refuse would be asking for trouble. Simon did not hesitate. He came forward, looked sympathetically at Jesus, then lifted the beam onto his shoulder. 'Move on there,' shouted the centurion to the soldiers in front. The procession moved off once more.

When they reached the hill for execution, the prisoners fell down with exhaustion once the beams were removed from their shoulders. The centurion dismissed Simon, but Jesus was able to look at him, and Simon knew that the man was genuinely grateful. The post holes were cleared first of all by the soldiers. Afterwards the beams were laid flat on the ground and the cross pieces dove-tailed on top. The bolts were driven through the holes in the beams and made secure.

While this was happening, it was the custom to allow victims a drink containing a mild drug that would help the pain. The two criminals drank it lustily, but Jesus refused. The men were then stripped naked, the final indignity and shame for a Jew, and the garments thrown to one side. When the crosses had been checked by the centurion, the prisoners, in turn, were laid onto each cross, their feet resting on a small piece of wood which would keep them upright. One of them shouted and cursed at the soldiers. One of them cried and pleaded for mercy. Jesus lay there quiet and still. First of all their hands were tied tightly to the beams, then their ankles were tied to the main beam. There was a gasp from the crowd when a soldier raised the hammer for the first nail to be banged home. Each of the two prisoners screamed in agony as the nails went in. When it was the time for Jesus, the soldier hesitated but then drove home the nails. Jesus summoned up all His self-control and He only winced and shook as the nails went through His hands and ankles. He spoke weakly, 'Father, forgive them. They do not realise what they are doing.'

One of the soldiers took the wooden plaques that he had been given, apparently ordered by the Governor himself, and they were nailed onto the top of the crosses. But the worst was yet to come. When the centurion was satisfied that the criminals were secure, each crucifix in turn was lifted by the soldiers and the foot of the main beam was laid at the edge of the post hole. Then, with one push, the crucifix was raised higher and, with a huge dull thud, the main beam went down into the hole. Each prisoner screamed in agony as the pain from their bodies pressing down on the nails became impossible to bear. Each one passed out.

Jesus was in the centre of the three, and the biggest cheer of all three had been when His cross had thudded into the hole in the ground. It was only nine o'clock in the morning, but the excitement was now over. Soon some of the crowd drifted away back towards the city. For the soldiers this was the worst part, the long wait while the crucified died. They amused themselves by gambling.

Clothes were useful for spare money for they could easily be sold. When they went through the criminals' clothes, there was little to excite the soldiers until they came to the outer garment of Jesus. Though bloodstained, it was still in one piece and was worth more than anything they had ever come across. The gambling became intense as they challenged each other   for this prize.

At this point, the representatives of the Jewish authorities, and a group of Pharisees, Rabbis, and Lawyers, arrived at the scene. They pushed their way forward. When they reached the front, they gloated over Jesus and enjoyed their triumph. Playing to the crowd they taunted Him. 'He saved others! Now let Him perform a miracle and save himself.'

Some of the crowd laughed and jeered, as cowards often will under these circumstances. Encouraged by this, one of the representatives challenged Jesus. 'You said you were going to tear down the Temple and rebuild it in three days. Well then, now is the time to do it. We'll give you three days to succeed.' There was more laughter and more jeering. Then suddenly, one of the Pharisees pointed to the plaque above the head of Jesus. There were words, in fact in three different languages, Hebrew, Latin, and Greek. One of them read the Hebrew, 'King of the Jews'. 'How dare he,' said the senior Pharisees present, meaning Pilate, and immediately sent a message to the High Priest. They all followed, having shouted a protest to the centurion about the plaque. All left the scene except one who was detailed to keep an eye on the proceedings. The authorities were taking no chances about the disciples of Jesus and what they might do with Jesus when He was dead.

After a brief consultation at the home of the High Priest, a strongly worded protest was delivered by hand to the Governor. 'At least,' the High Priest had written, 'let it read "he claimed to be...".'. The reply was curt. 'What I have written, I have written.' There was nothing that anyone could do about it.

Back at the site of crucifixion, one of His fellow crucified challenged Jesus. 'Save yourself, you idiot. And while you are doing it, save us as well.'

'Shut up!' shouted the other one. 'Show some respect. We deserve this, but He doesn't.' Turning his head towards Jesus, he said, 'If you are the son of God, then remember me when you meet Him in the next world.' Jesus smiled, even through His pain. 'Don't worry,' He replied. 'Even now, your faith, such as it is, has helped you. Today, you and I will be in Paradise together.'

There was little to watch now, so more and more of the crowd left. At this point, a group of people, mourners, arrived, and those at the front of the remaining crowd made way for them to come forward. There was Mary, the mother of Jesus, two sisters who had travelled with her from Galilee, Mary, the wife of Cleopas, and Mary from Magdala. The disciple John was with them. It was John who had sent a message to his father to pass on to Mary in Nazareth, inviting her to share in the triumph of Jesus her son, for he had believed that this last trip to Jerusalem was to be the time for the establishment of the Kingdom. Instead, here she was, in mourning, gazing up at her dying son.

The crucified occasionally asked for a drink as they went in and out of consciousness while they were dying. In one of those moments, Jesus called out for a drink. One of the women delegated to do this, looked at the centurion asking for permission. He nodded, and she lifted a sponge soaked in the drugged wine to the lips of Jesus, and then to the other two. Jesus opened His eyes. As He gazed down He was amazed to see His mother, Mary, standing nearby. He tried to smile but it was difficult. He recognised the others beside her, particularly John with whom He had had such a close relationship. Summoning up all His remaining energy, He said to His mother, 'Mother, now you have a new son,' meaning John. His voice was barely audible. He then looked at John. 'Now,' He said, 'you have a new mother.' The effort was too much. The pain was intense. Once more He resorted to Joseph's training. Once more the words of the Psalmist came naturally. 'My God, my God, why hast Thou abandoned me? I have cried desperately for help but still it does not come.' He mumbled on, but little could be understood. 'My strength is gone... My throat is as dry as dust... They gamble for my clothes and divide them among themselves... All nations will remember...' and, mercifully, once more He lost consciousness. John, his arm around Mary, held her tight.

All of them were united in their grief.

It was now nearly mid-day, but, instead of the sky being bright, it was getting dark. There were those who anticipated a storm, and they left in a hurry to return to the city. There was an eerie silence. Suddenly the body of Jesus shuddered violently. Everyone looked at Jesus. He was smiling. With all the energy He had left, He said, 'It is over!' His head dropped. Jesus had died. The women wept aloud. Even the centurion looked up, got up and checked that Jesus was dead. He pierced Jesus's side with his sword. There was no reaction. He said to his men, 'Do you know, I think He might well have been the son of God.' One of the other criminals had already died. It was not long before the crucifixion would be over. The storm that had threatened now arrived. Thunder echoed around the hills, and flashes of lightning lit up the city buildings. It was reported later that there had been some damage, even in the Temple itself.

The final act was about to take place. Unknown to the family, Joseph from Arimathea, respected by both the Sanhedrin and the Roman Governor, had asked the Governor if the body of Jesus could be taken down from the cross and buried before the Passover began. Pilate was surprised to hear that Jesus was already dead, and sent for a senior officer to confirm the fact. When this confirmation was received, Pilate agreed to Joseph's request.

As the storm passed, carefully and tenderly, Joseph approached John the disciple as he sheltered with the other mourners near the site of the crucifixion. He showed him the consent form that he had received from the Governor's office. John introduced Joseph to Mary and explained his kind offer. She was glad, and learnt that Joseph's private burial ground was not far away. He, and his servants, had already brought with them a large linen sheet. Joseph approached the centurion, showed him the consent form, and, with the help of the soldiers, took down the body of Jesus. Then, in solemn procession, the body of Jesus was carried away and into the cemetery. A grave cave had already been prepared without knowing who would be the occupant. Jesus's body was laid to rest, the entrance to the tomb sealed, and they all stood for a few moments in silence and then made their way back to Jerusalem. There was no time to prepare the body for proper burial for it was nearly six o'clock, the beginning of the Sabbath. This would now have to be done after the Passover Day was over. So John escorted Mary and the other women back into the city to the home of John Mark, rather than taking them to the disciples' camp on the Mount of Olives where they had been the night before.

CHAPTER 7

SATURDAY

EVEN at the tomb, there could be no freedom for Jesus. The representative from the Sanhedrin had followed at a discreet distance, and then hurried to tell Caiaphas what had been done. After more consultation, the High Priest ordered that guards should be placed at the entrance to the tomb.

The Sabbath passed quietly for the followers of Jesus. Most of the disciples, including Peter, had surreptitiously seen the crucifixion without revealing to anyone else that they were there. There were, therefore, some tormented souls who made their way back to the camp in the darkness. As they met, each had a story of shame to tell, including Peter. It sounded more like a confessional. But the greatest torment was for Judas. His mixture of passion and lust for political violence had brought him frustration during these last two years, for Jesus could have been the leader the nationalists needed. His last effort at goading Jesus into acting had back-fired on him. Now he was branded a traitor. Hated by the followers of Jesus. Mocked by the authorities. He threw away the money he had received, in disgust with himself, and he threw away his life.

Late in the evening, when the Sabbath was over, the women began their preparations for the anointing of the body of Jesus.

Nicodemus had brought spices to Joseph, and asked that his servant might be sent with the gift to Mary, the mother of Jesus. Joseph gladly performed this small task. During the evening, the Twelve, apart from Judas, and John who was already there, arrived at the home of John Mark. They talked late into the night, afraid in case the Temple police would come and arrest them as well, then they slept.

CHAPTER 8

SUNDAY

WHEN the first light of day filtered through to those in the house where they were staying, the three Marys, together with Joanna and Salome, made their way out of the city gate and into the private cemetery. Not one of them had thought how they were going to move the stone standing at the entrance of the tomb until they were nearly there. They found the tomb, at least they thought they had, for when they got there the stone door had been rolled to one side, and when they looked inside the tomb it was empty. 'Some one has stolen the body,' one of them said. 'Perhaps Joseph moved the body yesterday,' another suggested. 'Are you sure this is the right one?' asked a third. Mary, Zebedee's wife, the one who had travelled with Mary, the mother of Jesus, from Galilee, asked the other Mary from Magdala who was younger than the rest of them, to run and tell the other disciples. Mary ran as fast as she could.

The disciples were shocked at the news, but also amused. 'You know what women are like,' said Matthew, assuming that they had got lost and could not find the right tomb. However, Mary was insistent, so Peter and John set off for the tomb. They too ran as fast as they could, while Mary walked at her own pace. John reached the tomb first of all, looked inside from the entrance but did not go in. Peter, however, did not hesitate but went straight inside. It was cold and dark but there was enough light to see that the grave clothes of Jesus had been folded up and placed on the burial slab as if someone had got up and left of their own accord. John followed Peter into the tomb, saw the folded clothes and sat down on the slab. 'By all that is holy, He has come back to life just as He said He would. There is such a thing as resurrection.'

'Let us make sure first of all,' Peter said, 'before we tell the women. It would be wrong to rouse Mary's hopes.' John agreed. 'He's not there,' said Peter to the women. 'We'll make enquiries.' The women made their way back into the city while Peter and John went to see if Joseph knew what had happened. As the women were leaving the cemetery, Mary of Magdala was returning. The others explained what had happened and what they were now doing. Mary from Magdala said that she would like to go back into the cemetery and spend some time enjoying the peace and quiet.

By now the sunshine was bright and in her eyes as she walked along. A shadow appeared in front of her, and she made out the features of a man. Her immediate reaction was to assume that He was one of the gardeners. 'Excuse me,' she said. 'We came to embalm the body of Jesus, but it is no longer there. Can you tell me, please, where they have put the body?'

The man was not the gardener, but Jesus, raised from the dead. He said to her, 'Mary'. Instantly she knew who it was. No-one spoke her name as He did. She shielded her eyes from the sun, recognised who it was and threw herself at His feet, kissing His feet and crying for sheer joy. 'Master,' she said with great wonder. Jesus knelt down and lifted up her head. 'You are the first to know the truth. Now go back into the city and tell the others what you have seen. Tell them that I will come and see them later in the day.' She launched herself at Him, holding Him, making sure that this was not a dream, not an hallucination.

'It really is you!' she said. She had never known such joy.

'Now go and tell the others,' said Jesus with a little more force while smiling at her shock and joy. Mary ran back into the city. Passers-by wondered what on earth could demand such exertion. Mary burst into the room where the disciples were sitting. Nearly out of breath, she tried hard to tell them what had happened. When they got her to calm down and say everything again slowly, not one of them believed her. It was only when Peter and John arrived after their visit with Joseph and told their part of the story, that they began to believe her. 'He will meet you here this evening,' she said.

Mary, the mother of Jesus, had tried to rest but could not. She too went back to the cemetery. She wanted to be with her son, wherever He was. She found a quiet place to sit. Without her realising it, someone came and sat beside her. When she became conscious of someone sitting there, she turned, startled by the realisation. 'Hello Mother,' said Jesus. Mary fainted into His arms. When she recovered, she could not believe her eyes. She held His hands, and neither said a word.

Then, when she had fully recovered from the shock, the two of them talked together for quite some time, going back to the beginning and throughout His life. She asked about the future and He answered her carefully so that she might truly understand. She was the only one who had known Him from the very beginning. It was right that she should know the ending of the story.

There was an atmosphere of excited anticipation in the room where Jesus and the Twelve had shared the Passover meal. They were still afraid however, for they had been talking about the arrest in the Garden of Gethsemane. The doors were locked, just in case. All of them, except Judas of course, were there. Thomas, always the man who needed reassurance, waited impatiently. At last his patience left him. 'This is foolishness,' he said. 'We all saw Him dead on the cross. No-one comes back to life. Mary was probably overcome with emotion and thought she saw Him. I am not going to be made to look foolish.' And, before anyone could move, he left the room.

Eventually, Jesus appeared. They were stunned. The fact was that the door had not opened, and yet Jesus was standing there and obviously no ghost. As if to prove the point and answer any doubts that they had, Jesus asked for something to eat. There were so many questions in their minds, but now they could not speak. In a way they were in shock. Gradually they got over their initial reaction, and Jesus began to teach them about what had happened and why. It was like going back in time. When He had finished and answered all their questions, He called for them to pray. They knelt down, closed their eyes, and were moved as Jesus prayed for them. When there was silence, they opened their eyes. Jesus was no longer there.

Meanwhile, back on the hillside, the camp had broken up and everyone was on their way home. There was a mood of sadness and disappointment. They had no idea yet what had really happened, but before long Jesus would meet them again in their own homes and they would know the truth.

For example, Cleopas and Symeon, two of those who had been converted by Jesus during His Samaritan ministry and had been staying at the camp on the Mount of Olives, were now, like everyone else, going home, for the Festival was over. They were having a heated discussion about Jesus, who He really was and what had happened to Him. 'It does not make sense,' said Symeon. There were a number of people on the road, for the city had been packed with visitors. A man joined them as they walked along, but He did not interrupt their conversation at first. Then, at an appropriate moment in the conversation, the man, Jesus, asked them, 'who are you talking about?'

They stood still and looked at the stranger, not realising that it was Jesus. 'Are you the only person that has been in Jerusalem for the last few days and not heard of the executions? Why, we are talking about Jesus from Nazareth. We believed that He was the Messiah, the son of God. Now, having seen Him executed as a common criminal, it seems we must have made a mistake.'

'Not necessarily,' Jesus countered. Then He began to talk about God, the creation of the world, His gift of Free Will, the disobedience of humanity, and in particular the People of God, the Jews. He quoted the prophets, giving examples of God's call to repentance and the reluctance of the Jewish people to do His will. He quoted especially from Isaiah and the section of the scriptures where the prophet describes the Messiah as a suffering Messiah, despised and rejected, beaten and killed like a sheep for sacrifice.

'Well that all makes sense now,' said Cleopas reluctantly, but impressed by the man's obvious knowledge of scripture.

'Yes, but what of the rumours that we heard today? There are those suggesting that He has risen from the dead!' he exclaimed.

They were now entering the village of Emmaus where they

lived. The man with them was about to leave them when they invited Him to stay the night. A meal was soon prepared and, out of courtesy, Cleopas invited the visitor to ask God's blessing on their food. Jesus took the bread, lifted it, and gave thanks to God. Then He said, 'I am the Bread of Life.' Suddenly, as if a blindfold had been taken off, the two men realised who it was. They looked at one another, and then at Jesus again. However, by the time they looked, He had disappeared.

'How stupid we were!' exclaimed Symeon. 'We should have known who it was with that knowledge of scripture. It was inspiring. He has kindled that flame of belief in me once more.' They ate their meal quickly and then returned to Jerusalem as fast as they could in order to tell the other followers that they had seen Jesus.

CHAPTER 9

MONDAY ONWARDS

JESUS appeared to all His disciples so that they would know once and for all who He was. The Twelve were uncertain what to do. They were like a cohort of soldiers waiting for instructions, or like a group of escaped prisoners scared to make a move. One day, Thomas returned. Immediately they told him about Jesus's visit and the other disciples who had seen the risen Lord. Thomas was not moved. 'Unless I see for myself the marks in His hands where the nails were hammered, or the gash in His side where the centurion thrust his sword, I shall not believe you.' In spite of all their protestations, he would not believe them, and left later that day unconvinced.

Some time later, when Thomas was with the Twelve, Jesus unexpectedly appeared. He stood by Thomas who was totally non-plussed. 'Thomas,' said Jesus kindly, 'look at my hands. See the nail prints? See my side where the sword entered. I want you, of all people, to believe for yourself.'

Thomas needed no such proof. He simply fell to his knees at the feet of Jesus and said reverently, 'My Lord. You are indeed God.'

'Thomas,' said Jesus, 'you believe because you have seen me for yourself. How much more wonderful will it be for those who believe in me and yet will never have seen me.'

They all agreed with a strong 'Amen'. Jesus now assumed the authority of a father. 'Go home. Go and see your families and tell them what has happened. Catch up on their news. Be ready to say 'Good-bye' to them for you may not see them again for quite some time. The time for your work to begin is at hand. I will come and see you near Galilee.' And as suddenly as He came, so He left.

Because they were still afraid of the authorities and their spies, the disciples left the city at night and travelled up country, and eventually went their separate ways.

By now, rumours about Jesus being alive again were circulating through the city. The news was passed on to Caiaphas the High Priest and he, in turn, summoned those responsible for setting the guard on the cemetery. When those persons arrived, he asked what had happened. 'Well, sir,' they said, 'the guards ran away. They left their post. During the night they got scared, which is understandable. They say they heard noises, like tomb stones moving, and ran away.' The High priest was annoyed but there was little that he could do now.

After a short consultation with others, he said, 'Pay the guards some money and order them to say that during the night the followers of Jesus came and stole the body.' He sat back in hope rather than satisfaction.

It was several days later, when Peter and some of the others had met by the lake of Galilee in the evening, that he stated, 'I am going fishing!'

'We'll go too,' they said. So Peter, Thomas, Nathaniel, James, and John, and two others, loaded a boat with fishing gear and set out onto the lake. They fished all night, but caught nothing. As the dawn appeared, they saw a nearby beach and someone standing at the water's edge.

The man cupped His hands and, as He shouted, His voice echoed over the water. 'Have you caught anything, boys?' He said.

'No, nothing,' Peter shouted back, 'and we have been out fishing all night.'

'Then cast your net on the right hand side of the boat and trawl there,' shouted the man on the beach.

They did so and struck such a shoal of fish that they could hardly pull in the net. Suddenly Peter had that sense of déja vu. He knew who the stranger was. 'It is the Lord,' he yelled. He tucked up his clothes, swung his feet out of the boat, and waded to the shore. The rest of them hurriedly pulled in the nets and started to paddle towards the beach. When Peter reached the beach, he saw that Jesus had already made a fire and had brought some bread with Him.

'Bring me some fish,' He said to Peter. Peter did so as soon as the boat was near enough. Expertly He gutted the fish and gave them to Jesus on stick spears to cook over the fire. The others pulled the boat up on to the beach, and then started to sort the fish. There were over a hundred, and some of them were really big fish. When the fish were cooked, Jesus called to them to come over to the fire. They sat round and Jesus said grace. Then He broke the bread and the fish and gave them some. They all remembered the last supper where He had shared with them in a similar way. When they had finished, Jesus asked Peter to walk with Him.

This was the first time that they had been alone together

since His arrest. Peter wanted to apologise for his cowardice, but he was so ashamed that he did not want to talk about it. Jesus asked him, 'Peter, do you love me?'

'Lord, you know that I love You,' Peter replied forcibly.

'Then take care of those who are young in the faith,' Jesus said. There was silence as they walked on. Peter was trying to find the significance in Jesus's words. A few paces further on, Jesus again asked Peter, 'Peter, do you truly love me?'

'Lord, you know that I love You,' Peter reiterated, puzzled by the repeated question.

'Then take my place as the shepherd and feed my flock,' Jesus continued. Even further down the beach, Jesus again turned to Peter and asked him, 'Peter, do you love me more than anyone else in the world?'

Now Peter had missed the significance of the whole exercise. His Galilean impatience was rising. 'Lord, You know everything. You know my heart. Yes, I love you!' he exclaimed.

Jesus shook His head at Peter and smiled at his lack of understanding. 'Then take care of my followers.'

They turned and walked back in silence. They sat down, and Jesus was ready to answer any questions that the disciples had. Among them were these.

'Lord,' asked Matthew, 'when will you establish your kingdom and give freedom to our people?'

'That is not for any of us to know', replied Jesus. 'But when you are aware of the Spirit of God, He will guide you as to what and when things will happen.'

James asked Him, 'when your Kingdom is established on earth, who will share in the running of your Kingdom? Shall we be sitting on the right and left of your throne?'

Jesus replied, 'That is not for me to decide. But in my Kingdom, may I remind you, the first shall be last and the last shall be first. Those who follow me now, taking up my cross of suffering if necessary, will be the greatest in the Kingdom.'

Soon afterwards Jesus left them.

Later that day, Andrew asked Peter what he and Jesus had been talking about.

Peter, still a little put out, said, 'He asked me three times whether I loved Him or not!'

Andrew asked, 'Three times?'

'Yes,' said Peter. Andrew smiled and shook his head at Peter. 'What?' asked Peter.

Andrew explained. 'What did you do three times?'

Peter suddenly realised. He dropped to his knees. 'Lord, how could I be so stupid.' There and then He prayed, thanking God for His goodness and rejoicing in His recommission.

Jesus appeared to the disciples from time to time during the next few days, encouraging them, guiding them, reassuring them. However, there had to come a time when He would cease to appear. The responsibility for the future was theirs. The particular tasks of resurrection ministry were now over.

For the last time, Jesus asked them all to meet together. It was to be on the Mount of Olives at the point where He had begun His journey down the hill to the city of Jerusalem. This was to be the starting point of their new journey. So, about ten days later, soon after dawn, having camped out overnight, the disciples stood together nervously, and yet with an excited anticipation. Jesus appeared and greeted them. 'Peace be with you.'

They responded, 'And also with you.'

'Now I must take my leave of you all. I have thanked my Father that He gave you to me and I have tried hard to take care of you, and to prepare you for the work that lies ahead. I have been given full authority to commission you in God's work. Beginning from Jerusalem, now I send you out into the world. You have seen the vision of God's Kingdom. You know that your task is to build that Kingdom here on earth, working with God, and wherever He may send you. Go and make disciples, giving them the opportunity of a new beginning to their lives through their repentance and through baptism. Teach them how to live as citizens in this new Kingdom, using me as your example.

'Soon I shall leave you and you will never see me again. But trust me. Stay here in the city and soon God my Father will send you His Spirit and you will experience a power that you have never experienced before. You will be able to do all that I have done, and perhaps even greater things. And, last of all, you will not be alone for you will realise, in a wonderful way, that I am with you, in spirit, every moment of every day.'

Then Jesus approached each one in turn. He put His hands on their shoulders, embraced them and kissed them on both cheeks, saying their names as He did so. 'Thaddaeus; Simon; James; Matthew; Thomas; Bartholomew; Philip; James; Andrew.' To Peter He said, 'Bend down Peter so that I can kiss you.' Tears were rolling down the cheeks of the big Galilean as he bent down. Jesus embraced him, kissed him, and let him go. 'Take care of them, Peter. You are now their Shepherd.' Finally He came to John. 'John,' He said in such a loving voice. They embraced.

Jesus held up His hands to pray and the disciples knelt

where they were for prayer. 'Oh, God my Father. Thank You for these men; for their faith; for their love; for their willingness to offer their all for You. Guide them, guard them, bless them, empower them.' Jesus then looked at them in prayer. 'God bless you, each one.' There was silence. When the disciples looked up, Jesus had gone. For a few moments they looked at one another, bewildered. Then, with a great feeling of joy and togetherness, they embraced each other.

The challenge of Jesus was over. Now the challenge was theirs.

Made in the USA
Charleston, SC
04 March 2016